S0-BJU-249

DRAGON BONES IN THE YELLOW EARTH

Dragon Bones

in the Yellow Earth

By JAMES AND IRVING CRUMP

Illustrated with drawings, maps and photographs

DODD, MEAD & COMPANY

NEW YORK

Copyright © 1963 by James and Irving Crump

All rights reserved

No part of this book may be reproduced in any form
without permission in writing from the publisher

Library of Congress Catalog Card Number: 63-10253

Printed in the United States of America
by The Cornwall Press, Inc., Cornwall, N. Y.

Dedicated
to the memory of the late
ROY CHAPMAN ANDREWS
good friend and great explorer

Preface

The authors wish to caution the reader immediately that this book is written by and for amateurs; since Crump *père* is an author and editor by profession (and a fly-fisherman by inclination) and Crump *fils* professes Chinese language and literature (also a fly-fisherman by inclination), it follows, then, that neither could be a professional archeologist or paleontologist, though both have attended most of the archeological events of the last century via armchair and desk lamp. Because this is primarily a narrative of the field work of professionals, there is little here which is new to scholars; the last chapter, however, may provide information for those who do not read Chinese.

Besides having a proprietary feeling for the bits and pieces of ancient man and his works, wherever they may be, the authors have had close ties with China through the career of one and the friendships of both. This book is the outcome of their mutual interest in and zest for the ancient history and prehistory of that area of the world and the fascinating sense of romance and treasure trove which infuses so many of the discoveries made there. In addition, the authors have long felt that the work of professionals, both Chinese and Western, should be made more accessible to the public at large.

J. and I. C.

Contents

Illustrations

PHOTOGRAPHS

Following page 82

Natives searching for Shang bronzes

*Farmer, diggers, and dealers holding conference to determine
price and method of protecting valuable bronze*

Fragment and ink-rubbing of genuine oracle-bone inscription

Two forgeries of oracle-bone inscriptions

*Preliminary exploration of fissure later known as cave of Peking
Man*

Looking WNW at the Chou-k'ou Tien site from across the valley

Removing the contents of an oracle-bone pit

*Cutting away the earth below a priceless bronze vessel while
measuring its exact location and attitude*

Painted Pottery bowl from Pan-p'o Ts'un near Sian

*Pounded earth foundations and pillar foundations at the Shang
City site*

Priceless Shang bronzes

DRAGON BONES IN THE YELLOW EARTH

Ghouls and Old Bones

1

The ghoulish art of grave robbing and the ceaseless quest for dragon bones have been national pastimes of the peasantry of China since the beginning of human history in the land of the yellow earth. With banditry, which ranked close behind them both as a profitable avocation, the Chinese farmers often managed to add a few copper coins to their meager annual incomes. And of course there was always the exciting possibility that some dark night on ancient graveyard exploration they might make a valuable find and in one stroke become comparatively rich; that is, if they were not caught and beheaded for their crime.

With the coming of communism, banditry has lost a lot of its possibilities for quick wealth. For one thing, there are no longer any unprotected caravans to be surprised and robbed. There is little merchandise to be stolen and no one has enough wealth to make looting worthwhile. Besides, nothing sums up the present plight of China better than the words of a Chinese earnestly explaining the New China to a foreign acquaintance: "Look at what we have done for ourselves since the Liberation," he said. "We used to be a corrupt state full of bandits and now there are no more bandits at all—since everyone knows what everyone else is doing all the time, who could be a bandit?"

To a great degree this system of spying on each other probably applies to the practice of grave robbing too, but since ghouls have nearly always carried on their stealthy activities individually or in closely knit family groups and mostly at night, the chances of detection and exposure are greatly reduced. And although the hazards have been increased since the advent of communism, grave robbing is still clandestinely carried on in many sections of China, particularly where pockets of resistance groups are active.

The problems of disposing of the loot recovered from rifled tombs have become increasingly more numerous and the operation much more dangerous, but still there seem to be ways known only to the grave robbers of successfully selling their booty. True, now and then a few culprits are caught in the act of trying to smuggle "National Treasures" out of the country or in other ways converting the bronzes and other types of funeral furniture into cash but, despite the fatal penalties these unfortunates pay, the practice of looting ancient tombs still goes on. One of the most amazing stories of grave robbing that has come to light under communism concerns the ghoulish adventures of one Mr. Chi and his desecration of a tomb that became known officially as Tomb No. 406 to the Ministry of Science's Institute of Archeology. Through the grave robber's confession and "self-criticism" the Ministry of Science was able to locate the tomb in 1951 and carry on further archeological exploration and render a complete report on the discovery of the unhappy Mr. Chi.

On a very black night toward the end of 1948, so the story goes, the potential tomb despoiler carefully made his way along a narrow footpath leading north from Ch'angsha up Wu-li P'ai, a slight hill rising from the plain. He walked silently on straw-soled sandals. Over his shoulder he carried a heavy mattock and a long spadelike shovel. He was familiar with every inch of the path and had no trouble finding his way in spite of the darkness. He was able to sense each slight bend and he knew exactly when he reached the vicinity of two low, weed-covered mounds of earth somewhat to one side of the footway. Here he paused to listen and to peer into the darkness, for he wanted to make absolutely sure that no one was following him. He also wanted to locate himself exactly, for much depended on that. Moving carefully off the main path, he felt his way silently toward the flat area between the low mounds. He had farmed in this general vicinity all his life and he knew almost by instinct each rise and depression of the whole hill.

Some time each year between harvest and planting he had prowled this rise with an exploratory eye, for it was a well-known fact, verified by the old ones thereabout, that ages ago—millennia, in truth—this whole slope had been the burial place of royalty and people of high station. There were many stories told of tombs made of hard tamped earth—pounded earth, as the peasants termed it—dating back two thousand years and more (even before the Han dynasty) that had been found and opened. Veritable fortunes in bronzes and other relics of ancient times had been unearthed by local farmers and converted into currency, and the finders had lived in affluence ever after.

For generations fortunate ones had discovered slight, scarcely noticeable sunken places in the surface of the earth if they had good eyes and knew what to look for. These were known to the farmers as broken-wood pits or depressions and told the story of a rotted and collapsed coffin in a grave well below the surface. If there was evidence of tamped earth a few feet down, then there was unquestionably a tomb of some person of importance not too deep. In it would probably be found a treasure in objects of value buried with the deceased that would no doubt be well worth the labor of digging. Of course the treasure hunter would be risking arrest and possible execution if discovered in this act of ravishment, for the Nationalist Government did not approve of grave robbing either.

Of late years no one in the general vicinity of Wu-li P'ai had been able to discover any broken-wood depressions that were undisturbed, and the few disturbed ones that were stealthily opened and explored quickly proved that they were tombs that had been robbed long before. So interest in grave robbing had waned considerably and finally ceased, an unprofitable activity. But our nocturnal prowler up the dark slope was never convinced that the presence of these broken-wood pits or depressions was absolutely necessary to the establishment of the location of a tomb, for he reasoned that there might have been quite a few coffins made so stout that they would not collapse. He had seen evidence over the years while working in the yellow earth that some kinds of wood did not deteriorate. Instead, they seemed to take on something of an indestructible quality if they rested in the earth for a long time. If coffins were made of such stout stock, they would not rot and cave in and therefore there would be no telltale depression on the surface.

But the presence of pounded earth was essential to the location of a tomb because it was well known that all important Chinese tombs were made of tamped, hard-packed earth. So while Mr. Chi still searched for broken-wood depressions, he also looked and prodded and even bored in the ground with a long-handled earth auger for evidence of soil that had been pounded into a much denser mass than the ground surrounding it. It was such a place that he had found quite some time since in the flat area between the two low mounds toward which he was moving. Even these mounds by themselves suggested that a very long time ago the earth had been disturbed there by the hand of man.

Farmer Chi had kept very silent about his discovery, but surreptitiously, both by night and by day, he had observed that flat area under every possible condition. He noted that after hard rains, frequent at certain times of year in that section of China, the water would lie on the surface for a long time and evaporate rather than sink into the ground. This also was a very good sign, and Mr. Chi was almost convinced that he had found the location of an unopened tomb. But he discreetly kept his counsel. This was his secret, his ace in the hole, so to speak.

But now he needed it. The world, which to him was China, was collapsing. The shattered remnants of Chiang Kai-shek's troops had broken at the Yangtze and fled. The past was past, and who knew what the future held? This was the time for him to get what he could out of the earth, which had always been the source of all good things for him, and build a bulwark for himself and his family against the uncertainties that lurked behind the curtain of time.

Sufficiently far enough off the path now he encountered the two low mounds more by feeling with his feet than by sight. Softly shuffling in the grass, he located the exact position where he planned to commence digging and, laying down his spade, he swung his mattock and sank it with a soft chopping sound into the rubbery clay in front of him. Dissatisfied, he moved slightly forward and tried again. There was the same sound and the same feel to the earth. Again he tried still further from his first chop, and this time his hand—which knew through every finger the feeling of the earth—could tell that the quality of the soil had changed. He gave a small grunt of satisfaction and paused to consider.

The presence of the two low mounds on either side of the spot where he had chosen to dig suggested that they might cover old tombs and that if he dug into them he would discover tamped earth too. But they might be much deeper than the one he was sure he had found whose pounded earth was almost on the surface. He had long ago considered this and concluded that two mounds might have been made from earth cut away from a tumulus which had existed there before the two new tombs were made. Therefore, the one he had located would be the older and the treasures it contained be so much more valuable. Also with the mound removed and the hard-packed earth practically on the surface, the grave could not be too far below his sandals and thus less effort would be required to get into it. So he set to work digging at an angle toward the mound on his right. Feeling through his mattock the density of the earth, he continued downward and westward in a narrow trench which left just room enough for him to raise his heavy hoe above his head. This was backbreaking work; he had to shake the sticky clods from his blade almost every time he took a stroke.

After an hour's perspiring effort in the deepening slit trench he must have climbed out and carried lump after lump of clay around to the other side of the eastern mound to throw them into the weeds. It wouldn't do to scatter them around the west mound, for there was a house less than one hundred yards away—the house dogs of Ch'angsha had keen ears and loud barks. He probably returned to the trench and dug for another hour or so and then repeated the process. Now he had almost reached a depth of five feet and he had felt packed clay all the way. At the west end of the bottom of his trench, he began to dig a smaller hole with his shovel, still angling toward the base of the west mound. When he had almost used up his time for the night, his shovel struck wood.

He could not have done the entire job in one night; it is doubtful if he could have done it in two. So we see him abandoning his work temporarily, perhaps filling up his trench loosely with clods of clay and spreading weeds and straw over the excavation. It is not known that anyone else helped him or was even in on the secret as yet, so we should visualize him returning the next night with iron saw, a chisel and mallet, or a hatchet, because he must have discovered already that the wood of this coffin was as sound as the day it was lowered into the ground, almost as he had expected it would be. That was why no one had seen a telltale depression and that was probably why this burial had lain undisturbed for more than two thousand years.

When next he began work, he came to the heavy coffin itself and knew that his first gamble had paid off. But now he had to open this surprisingly sound sarcophagus in the most cramped quarters imaginable. He had by chance hit the coffin almost exactly at its southeast corner, so he knew how it lay. He must have tapped and thumped the wood as he tunneled across the top of it. For about six or eight inches as he moved toward the center of the coffin the wood gave out a dishearteningly solid sound. Then, as he moved beyond the frame of the outer coffin and before he came to the inner coffin, he heard the hollow sound left by the space between them.

Whether he knew what to expect or whether he simply began cutting where the hollow sound was to be heard, we shall never know. Whatever the case may have been, he had hit on the place where most of the funeral furnishings were put as surely as though he had had a plan of the burial. (See sketches.) Having pulled away the coarse matting material with which the entire outer coffin had been wrapped, he chopped and sawed through the flat surface of this water-logged, solid wood until he had a hole big enough to get his arm and shoulder into the space between the *kuan* and the *kuo*—the inner and outer coffins. He took out all the things he could reach with his hands and with a hooked stick. He later claimed that a lacquer shield and a bronze sword were first; next came a dozen lacquer goblets large and small. Four bronze jugs of the *hu* type and four more of the *fang* style were next. A large bronze dish, four pottery tripods and eight of the spherical pottery containers called *tui* followed. And finally, at the furthest stretch of his stick, he hooked out a lacquer platter—at least, that's how he remembered it.

By this time he knew the plan of the double coffin exactly and realized that if he were to get at the rest of the booty he would have to tunnel across the top of the huge outer casket until he came to the hollow space on the other side. This he proceeded to do. The hard clay made it perfectly safe against cave-in, but how he managed to extract all the articles he did in the cramped space he dug for himself is a puzzle. Having reached the area which gave off a hollow boom, he again cut through and cleaned out what was to be reached. This side was somewhat of a disappointment after the treasures of his first opening. The only bronze he found was a dagger-ax

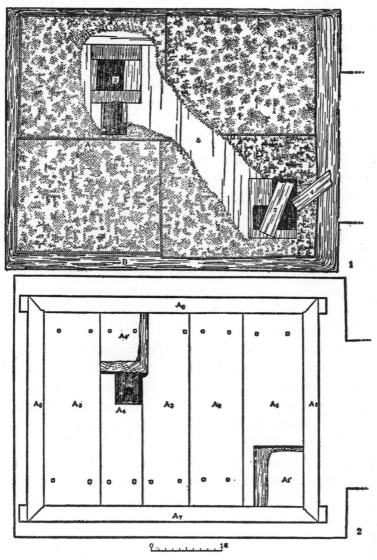

Top view sketch of coffin in tomb 406, showing path of tomb robber across the coarse matting (top); the mitered construction of the outer coffin (bottom)

complete with remains of the handle (if we can trust our source), which he took. He also found the model of a boat. (The people of Ch'u, for it was a grave of that southern state, knew that a boat would be as useful as a chariot if the world beyond resembled their land of rivers, as it was supposed to.)

What he did next is nearly incredible and must have brought him more sore muscles than profit. He located himself over the inner coffin and began to chop, chisel and saw through three layers of the tough wood. Two of these layers were four inches thick. He started with a fairly wide hole at the top, but for lack of working space, by the time he reached the inside of the multiple-layered inner coffin (the only one of its kind so far ever found), he had barely room to insert his hand. This he did and found nothing but the decomposing bones of the skeleton housed in this masterpiece of the joiner's art—though he may also have found two jade *pi,* as he later recalled.

We know by implication that he managed to sell off all the articles and we can visualize him cherishing his nest egg while the world went to pieces around him. But he had no way of knowing how life was going to change when the party-member activists in blue coveralls began showing up with tales of a brave new world. Soon everyone was organized into relentless "criticism and self-criticism" groups which night after night goaded each other into spasms of guilt and fear. Day by day, the brave new world was born in blood. The crowd pilloried landlord Chang, his honor, Mr. Li, was shot in the back of the head for having been a "reactionary capitalist," and Mr. Wang was executed for collecting rent. And so it went.

The control grew firmer as mutual suspicion bred. Sooner or later someone would "confess" having sold off National

Reconstruction of tomb furnishings from the "confessions" of the tomb robber

Treasures. From whom did he get them? Mr. Chi. Now Mr. Chi (our tomb robber, of course) had better "confess" that he had been at fault, that he was trying hard to reform, and with the help of party members and the new order he would reform. The pressure of fear built up in Mr. Chi as steam in a boiler, and finally, like a safety valve opening suddenly, he blurted out his story and took the consequences. The punishment he received is not recorded, but this much had certainly happened before the end of 1951 when the working party from the Ministry of Science's Institute of Archeology appeared to do one of its first jobs of salvage archeology under communism. We quote from their report:

"Because this tomb had been robbed in the winter of 1948, only a lacquer shield, a bow, wooden lances . . . and some wooden tomb figures were left. Only the tomb figures and the wooden lances were still in their original positions. *We draw this figure showing disposition of the objects as it was told to us by the robber himself.*"

The italics are ours for obvious reasons. That a serious publication should include a reconstruction of the furnishings of a coffin and their disposition from the lips of a man who robbed the tomb two years before in a fever of haste and fear lest he be caught shows incredible naïveté on the part of the archeologists. Leaving this aside, however—that the archeologists themselves should not have thought it necessary to point out that a culprit will tell his interrogators exactly what they want to hear if they push him hard enough, makes it only too clear that the questioners had duped themselves by their faith in the reforming powers of the "dictatorship of the proletariat."

Happily, this same faith has been used as a screen behind which the Chinese people, especially the peasants, continue to practice many of their ancient customs and beliefs while they blandly nod their agreement and apparent acceptance of the slogans of communism. They have to mouth such aphorisms as "Forget yesterday and remember tomorrow," but as for letting these influence their traditional habits and their methods of thinking, they continue to be Chinese, which is to say they still cling to customs and beliefs that date back thousands of years. And not the least of these is their faith in the ancient nostrums and potions that have been part of the fabulous Chinese pharmacopoeia for millennia.

The list of startlingly strange and amazing substances that are supposed to have potent medicinal values when properly mixed with other ingredients, not the least of which are fear and credulity, would read like the contents of a witch's brew. For instance, most Chinese peasants have always known and thoroughly believed that powdered rhinoceros horn, ground tiger whiskers, snakes' skins, bat droppings and a host of other weird things, when properly prepared, have almost magical curative powers. Outstanding among all the strange medicines in which they have traditional faith is one known as the knife-point drug, which is said to be, of all things, powdered dragon bones! As much of this as can be scooped up on the point of a knife and washed down with a cup of tea is said to have almost unbelievable therapeutic qualities. The teeth of this mythical and highly revered creature are also considered by the peasants to possess many mysterious attributes which make them extremely valuable. Rubies are supposed to be petrified dragon's blood, while the creature's saliva, if any could be secured, possesses properties that make it an almost irresistibly seductive perfume.

Quite unlike the fearsome, fire-breathing dragons of Greek mythology and the legends of the Nordic, Teutonic and An-

glo-Saxon people, as well as those of Biblical times, the dragons of China were nearly always of a most benevolent
disposition. It was they who brought all things good and important to human welfare, including the very rain that fell
from heaven. When thunder rolled and lightning flashed,
angry dragons were supposed to be engaged in a mighty conflict behind the clouds. The causes of these celestial disagree-
ments were of no great concern to mundane creatures, but
the rain that almost inevitably followed most certainly was.

Since rain was more important than anything else to the
agricultural economy of China, there was scarcely a village
of any size that did not have a temple dedicated to Lung
Wang, the dragon king ruler over seas, lakes, rivers and rain.
A day was set aside to worship him, and great festivals were
held in his honor. Most important on these occasions were
the spirited races held between long boats shaped and painted
like dragons and manned by lusty paddlers. These contests
were supposed to symbolize the heavenly conflicts between
the smoke-breathing monsters behind the clouds, and they
were staged to bring rain at the beginning of the planting
season. And since the day dedicated to the festivals and races
was the fifth day of the fifth month of the Chinese year and
the beginning of the summer rainy season, the desired result
almost never failed to be produced.

Legends and mythological tales of dragons have enriched
the *Book of Records* compiled by sober Confucian historians,
and the *Book of Changes,* which preserves a tremendous
amount of dragon lore dating back to the beginning of the
first millennium B.C., if not before, but nowhere in all this
material is it possible to establish just exactly what a dragon
was. Probably the only sensible explanation of this coiling
mass of serpentine creatures in Chinese history is the one put

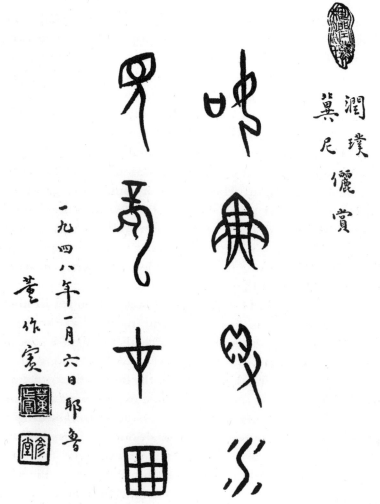

The left-hand line of large characters reads: "Seeing a dragon in the fields." The second character in the line is a pictograph meaning "dragon." The right-hand line reads: "Like a fish in water." The two phrases are from the Book of Changes and allude to good fortune and happiness, respectively.

forth by the late historian, Wen I-to. He assumes that very early in the history of the Chinese people there was a clan totem probably called a "dragon" which was serpentine in fashion (see sketch). The members of this totem grew more and more important and included nobility of varying degrees, including several emperors. And as the clan expanded, it absorbed more and more people of other clans.

We know from our northwestern Indians that when totems amalgamate, they tend simply to pile atop each other as on the totem poles. Thus when a clan or some other group of the horse totem, let us say, became affiliated with the dragon totem, the horse-dragon resulted; generally depicted as a serpent with a horse's head. In a similar way, other combinations came about, which explains why there were so many and varied forms of dragons.

It is of more than passing interest, however, to realize that among the numerous "peasant omens" recorded in the *Book of Changes* there are some that deal with the significance of seeing certain creatures on particular occasions. Among them we find, "When you see a dragon in the field, it is auspicious to see a superior"—as though one could expect to see a dragon around the next corner almost any day. Of course, the dragon population has dropped in England since the days of St. George, and perhaps the same fate has overcome the once common and friendly dragons of China. All of them have gone to their reward in heaven, no doubt. But a more reasonable explanation would be that folk memory and dialect names for creatures and things have swamped the identity of the creature originally known as a dragon so that now we have no way of knowing what the ancient Chinese were referring to when they "saw a dragon in the field."

Revered but also feared as the dragon always has been since

the beginning of civilization in China, it is quite apparent why the Chinese should attach very special medicinal virtues to the various parts of the creature's anatomy. For many centuries the apothecary shops in China have been selling, among their other quaint and curious medicines, dragons' teeth to drive out epilepsy, spasms, unrest of the heart, headaches, melancholia, fevers, madness and attacks of demons, not to mention liver diseases and infantile convulsions. As for dragon bones in powdered form, they have always been known to be efficacious in treating women's diseases, malaria, internal swellings, paralysis, convulsions, gallstones, fever, dysentery and many other afflictions.

The process of preparing dragons' bones for medicinal use has changed over the centuries. Time was when it was an elaborate and very mysterious procedure which, according to one scholar, provided for boiling the bones with certain powerful herbs, then grinding them into a fine powder which was packed into small silken bags. These in turn were stuffed into the body cavities of dead swallows from which the entrails had been removed. After remaining there overnight, the powder was taken out and mixed with certain other medicines before it was ready to be administered to the ailing one. Over the centuries this process no doubt changed a number of times and happily grew simpler. At one point it was reduced to where the bones were just soaked in some form of alcoholic spirits, and later even this preparation was abandoned and the dragons' bones were merely ground to a fine powder and administered, as mentioned before, on the point of a knife with a cup of tea as a chaser.

Faith in the curative powers of the teeth and powdered bones of the dragon made them commodities very much in demand among the Chinese peasants, so of course all of the apothecary shops carried them. And in spite of the fact that no one ever remembered that anyone had ever seen a dragon, much less killed one to make its bones available for medicinal use, there never seemed to be a dearth of them anywhere in China. The ailing peasants could buy all they needed, and for very little money.

There was a popular belief that dragons shed their bones as often as snakes shed their skins, and that these old bones were dug out of the ground by farmers and sold to the pharmacists. But all stories about dragon bones and where they were found and by whom were very vague and evasive. Indeed, no one really knew exactly where the supply came from save those who dug them out of the earth and a few of the apothecaries who dispensed them, and for very obvious reasons neither the diggers nor the purveyors would ever disclose their sources.

These bones and the dragons that were supposed to have shed them were of tremendous interest to western scientists who found their way to China shortly before the turn of the present century. But because of the antipathy toward the "foreign devils" that was building up during the nineties, resulting in 1900 in the uprising of the Boxers, whose motto was "Extermination of all foreigners," it was extremely dangerous for any westerner to attempt to penetrate very far into the interior. A German naturalist, Dr. Haberer, was among the first of a small group of western scientists to investigate the dragon bones that were medicinally of such manifest importance to the Chinese.

But he was unable to get very far in his efforts to find the source of these strange bones or to learn very much about them save the fact that various specimens were sold in the apothecary shops, the proprietors professing to know nothing about where they were found or by whom. The German naturalist was able to buy a number of dragons' bones in the drugstores of Peking and Shanghai and to examine them closely. He quickly saw that they were fossilized bones that had very evidently been buried in the earth for ages. And instead of coming from any creature that even remotely resembled the fire-breathing monsters of Chinese mythology, they were the bones of prehistoric creatures, mammals for the most part, many of which he was able to recognize.

Eagerly, Dr. Haberer set out to purchase as many of these bones as he could get, but soon his activities began to be viewed with suspicion by the Chinese pharmacists, and the available supply quickly dried up. But happily he had been able to acquire quite a sizable collection before his efforts were curtailed, and these he shipped to his good friend and associate, Dr. Max Schlosser, in Munich. This scientist became quite excited about dragon bones and proceeded to make a careful study of them, separating them into groups and identifying them as prehistoric mammals from the Tertiary and Pleistocene periods.

Ultimately Dr. Schlosser was able to establish the fact that the collection represented more than ninety different creatures, among them the saber-toothed tiger, the mastodon, the mammoth, the three-toed horse, and a variety of other animals long extinct. The German scientist wrote a scientific treatise on his study of the dragon bones entitled *Die Fossilen Saugethiere Chinas,* which became of tremendous interest to western scholars. Among other things, it revealed beyond a doubt that the inaccessible interior of China was a paleontological treasure house and there were any number of scientists who were willing to risk their lives to penetrate the fastness of the Celestial Kingdom for exploration purposes.

Few, however, were able to get the opportunity to do so because of the hatred of foreigners so evident there. In fact, it was more than a decade after Dr. Haberer had made his limited collection of fossilized bones before there was much if any effort to explore and study the paleontology and archeology of China. Among the first western scientists able to do so was a Swedish geologist and mining expert named Dr. J. Gunnar Andersson. He was asked by the Geological Survey of the Chinese Central Government to come to China for the purpose of searching out and evaluating geological formations that showed promise of commercial development.

Dr. Andersson, besides being a geologist and mineralogist with an international reputation, was also a paleontologist and an archeologist of rare ability and discernment. He had read Dr. Schlosser's treatise on the fossils that Dr. Haberer had collected by way of the apothecary shops, and on being invited to China, he decided to do a little exploring on his own, purely as an amateur. He did not then realize that he would have a part in some tremendously interesting discoveries, including the fossil remains of the most primitive man then known to science, who would be called Peking man, and that he would write a book about his adventures entitled *Children of the Yellow Earth* and his activities would establish him among the foremost students of the paleontology and archeology of China.

Dragon Bones 2

Dr. Andersson did not arrive in China until well after the turn of the century. He reached Peking in 1914 and made his headquarters in the government offices there. And although his hobbies of paleontology and archeology were in the back of his mind, he had to forget about them at first, for he faced a tremendous amount of work in his task of investigating the mineral deposits of China and surveying and evaluating their commercial possibilities. China was almost a virgin field for mining developments.

Of course, exploration and the discovery of mineral deposits, which was a major part of his job, took him far afield and gave him an opportunity to encounter fossilized bones in many places. As a result he quite naturally made an interesting collection of what his native workmen called "dragon bones." Indeed, they were pleased to discover his interest in such things, and when he offered them a few coppers for particularly well-preserved pieces, he soon found himself with a plethora of quite remarkable specimens.

With this collection, when he managed to find some spare time, Dr. Andersson was able to study and make some interesting notes about the prehistoric creatures that had inhabited China back to the Tertiary period in the earth's history. But he was not able to devote very much time to this and finally he shipped a large collection of fossilized bones off to his friend, Professor Wiman, at Upsala University in Sweden. Dr. Wiman was very enthusiastic about this opportunity to follow up Dr. Max Schlosser's studies of the bone specimens sent back by Dr. Haberer, and as a result Dr. Andersson kept him well supplied with material for study purposes.

But the geologist was not entirely happy with this arrangement either. In fact, he was a little irked by the fact that occasionally specimens and information came to him that he was certain, if studied at first hand in the field, would reveal a lot more information than he or Dr. Wiman could work out. He wrote this to the Swedish university professor. Dr. Wiman fully agreed with him. He too felt that there was a lot more to be learned from these fossilized bones and he deplored the fact that Dr. Andersson was not able to devote more time to their study and to the study and observation of the areas in which they were found. There were many exchanges of letters, no doubt, for Dr. Andersson was trying to correlate a lot of observations of his own with information about areas in which fossilized bones were found by the natives.

To carry on this effort, Dr. Andersson addressed a number of letters to the many missionary stations in northern China, asking in particular for any information that might lead to the location of the place where the main supply of dragon bones for the apothecary shops came from. He was sure there must be such a place, but of course he could not get any information about it from the pharmacists themselves or from the natives who dug up the bones and brought them in.

A number of these letters produced what looked like encouraging replies, some of which Dr. Andersson followed up to find interesting pockets of fossilized bone in the Tertiary deposits in different areas. But there were none that could be considered the source for the dragons' bones of commercial use. There were also many encouraging letters that could not be followed up because of the remoteness of the territory and the lack of time on the part of the otherwise very busy geologist. Meanwhile, back in Stockholm, Dr. Wiman was trying to solve Dr. Andersson's problem for him, and presently he came up with a very sound and gratifying solution.

On Dr. Wiman's staff at the university was a young, ambitious and very accomplished Austrian paleontologist, Dr. Otto Zdansky. Dr. Wiman talked with him at length and suggested that he take a leave of absence for two years and journey to China to become a member of Dr. Andersson's staff. The young scientist, realizing the opportunities for original study in China, became enthusiastic, and after the exchange of several letters between Dr. Wiman and Dr. Andersson, he started on the long journey from Sweden to Peking. He was welcomed with enthusiasm by Dr. Andersson, who had a number of interesting assignments for him.

Still the source of supply of dragon bones for all the drug houses and apothecary shops in northern China was uppermost in the mind of Dr. Andersson. So the first task he set for Dr. Zdansky after he got acquainted with China and her yellow earth was a widespread search for a big bone deposit capable of furnishing an inexhaustible supply. Since this was of great interest to the Chinese geological survey with which Dr. Andersson was connected, Dr. Zdansky began immediately to follow up leads that had been compiled as a result of Dr. Andersson's letters to the missionary stations.

Among the many clues furnished him, the young paleontologist was particularly interested in one location in northern China on the east bank of the Yellow River. It was the section known as Pao-te Hsien, where it was said some very interesting specimens were turned up by native bone diggers from time to time.

According to the information compiled by Dr. Andersson through letters and information he had gleaned from various sources, the natives of the little village of Chi-chia K'ou (located just inside the protective Great Wall of China) had for years been conducting what amounted to a mining operation in a primitive way for dragon bones, and although none of them would admit it, these natives were delivering to the drug buyers from the large cities an amazing amount of fossilized bones, some of which were excellent paleontological specimens.

The possibility of seeing these bone mines and studying the results of the efforts of the peasants inspired Dr. Zdansky to make Pao-te Hsien one of his first objectives. He started out with some misgivings, for he knew that these bone diggers were very secretive about their operations and not too friendly toward strangers, particularly westerners. But he had cannily been doing some investigation among drug houses and he managed to get some idea of the price that was being paid by the drug buyers for these dragon bones. It was a niggardly basis of payment; never more than a few coppers even for the best specimens, and he had an idea that he could probably buy the interest and willing cooperation of the bone diggers by doubling the amount of payment, which he could easily afford to do. That was his formula for establishing friendly relations with the inhabitants.

The district itself was a very interesting area constituting a great plateau riven by many steep-sided canyons that exposed huge layers of red clay. The plateau seemed to rest on a very large deposit of Paleozoic coal, some of which was being dug out by villagers for their own use. While Dr. Zdansky realized that the coal deposit would unquestionably be of interest to Dr. Andersson and would doubtless be investigated by him when its existence was reported, the young paleontologist was much more curious about the towering clay banks exposed by the deep ravines eroded in the plateau. These banks, some of them more than one hundred feet high, were pock-marked by small openings that were obviously the entrances to numerous tunnels.

On closer inspection Dr. Zdansky found that each tunnel (the openings were just about large enough for a man to crawl into) went deep into the plateau like the gallery of a mine, and each tapped one or more pockets of fossilized mammal bones. These pockets were scattered all through the clay, and except where some telltale evidence of their presence was exposed on the surface or in some washed-away section of bank, no one could tell exactly where they were located. In order to find these hidden pockets and recover the dragons' bones they contained, the diggers had developed an enterprising kind of mining operation which they had been carrying on for generations.

The operation was simple but cumbersome, and painstakingly slow. First the bone diggers would look for some surface clue that would suggest a pocket not too hard to reach and they would begin digging toward it. When they reached it and cleaned out this first pocket, they would continue tunneling in a blind way, gambling on reaching another pocket hidden somewhere deeper in the plateau. To Dr. Zdansky, this sightless method of exploring the red clay seemed far from efficient, but after he had been able to crawl through some of the narrow galleries and see how the digging was carried on, he realized that it was just about the only way the Chinese could explore the plateau. Moreover, it was not such a random effort as it at first seemed. The pockets of bone were numerous indeed and scattered in all directions through the huge clay deposit. In fact, if a man burrowed in almost any direction long enough, he was almost certain to find a number of pockets. And if, after a few days of digging, a worthwhile pocket was not opened up, the bone digger just started another tunnel in a totally different direction, confident that he would strike pay dirt, so to speak, in a very short time.

This method of searching for dragons' bones had been going on so long that some of the tunnels, twisting like ground mole galleries, extended into the plateau for as much as four hundred feet. Many of them represented the patient, back-breaking work of three or four generations of the same family, for this dragon bone digging had been going on longer than anyone could remember. The miners, who were farmers for the most part, devoted their winters to this kind of treasure hunting, but they always went back to their farming in the summer.

They had developed their own mining equipment, consisting of a short-handled pick for breaking out the chunks of clay that contained the fossils and an axe or hatchet for chopping the clay away from the specimens after they had been brought out of the tunnel. They used a small lantern, by the light of which they toiled in the narrow passage, and they had a tiny cart with very squeaky solid wooden wheels in which they brought their treasures out of the mine. They acted as their own mine mules, of course, and they had developed a harness for themselves to which the cart was attached by a long rope.

Dragging this behind them, they crawled into the tunnels to the point where they were working, and when they had a full load of chunks of bone-laden clay, they would creep back to daylight again, where they would get their haul ready for the drug buyers, meanwhile evaluating each piece carefully. They deemed themselves especially fortunate if they were able to bring out a skull or a section of jaw that contained teeth, for they were always able to demand more for these than for ordinary dragon bones. Since every peasant knew that a dragon's tooth had much more medicinal value than ordinary bone, the buyers were always willing to pay well for every tooth they could get, so the first thing the miner did in preparing his treasures for market was to break out all the teeth from both upper and lower jaws, with small regard for how much they broke up the bone. It would be ground up anyway, so it made no difference whether it came in big or little pieces.

When Dr. Zdansky saw how valuable specimens were being ruined from the ruthless treatment by the miners, he realized that the bone diggers had small respect for the remains of the benevolent patron of all Chinese, the dragon. This convinced the young paleontologist that the miners knew very well they were bringing to light the bones and teeth of creatures long buried in the clay, which in no way resembled the smoke-breathing bringers of rain and many other blessings. Many of the skulls and jawbones sufficiently resembled animals of the present to be at least vaguely identified even by ignorant peasant farmers who were well aware that no dragons were involved. Indeed, some with whom he was able to communicate smilingly agreed and explained that after all it wasn't

necessary for them to believe they were dragon bones, anyway. It was just the sick people who bought the medicine at
their neighborhood drugstore who had to have faith in the
nostrums that were sold to them.

Dr. Zdansky made haste to apply his economic formula for
establishing a friendly basis with the bone diggers. When he
saw a man chipping clay from a particularly fine specimen of
skull or jawbone, he would try to explain that he was ready
to pay him two or three times as much for his find as any of
the regular bone buyers, providing he took care not to injure
the specimen. He would also explain that he was making a
collection of fossilized bone for scientific study, and as a result it did not take the news long to spread among the bone
diggers. In a very short time all of the farmers thereabouts
became interested in looking for dragon bones for him. While
they did not comprehend very much about paleontology, they
definitely understood his better prices. He soon became wel-
come in all the mining tunnels and was amazed at the number of specimens that were brought to him for his inspection.
He made a remarkably fine collection with the expenditure
of comparatively little money. It included fossilized bone of
several different types of rhinoceri, a variety of elephants,
antelopes, three-toed horses, saber-toothed tigers, bears, pigs
and even giraffes. And he was quite sure that he had found
the source of supply of dragons' bones and dragons' teeth for
all the apothecary shops in northern China. The clay plateau
contained so many hidden pockets of petrified bone that the
farmers could continue their mining activities for another
hundred years without exhausting this natural storehouse.

Seeking to explain why the bones of prehistoric mammals
were gathered in pockets in the clay and so badly scrambled
together, Dr. Andersson suggested that all these creatures

once inhabited what were then great areas of steppes country. At frequent intervals these vast plains were visited by
disasters such as storms and cloudbursts that let loose deluges,
flooding the terrain and trapping hordes of creatures in gullies, and hollows and drowning them. Or, as another scientist
suggested, droughts or terrible grass fires started by lightning
flashes may have stampeded thousands of fear-crazed creatures
into wild flight to get beyond the reach of advancing walls
of flames. Panic could easily drive them all over some steep-
water-worn bank into a river where they would drown and
their remains become entombed in the clayey bottom. At any
rate, the scientists were all convinced that each collection of
bones was an evidence of the mass extinction of droves of
panic-stricken creatures by some natural calamity.

In the process of inspecting the mining developments of a
German engineer in the Meng-yin district of Shantung (in the
mountainous area south of Hsin-t'ai), Dr. Andersson had at
one time come across an exciting clue that he was sure would
lead to important paleontological discoveries. The German
mining engineer during his prospecting in the district had
discovered a sandstone ledge containing the fossilized vertebrae of a large creature which he could not identify. Nor
could Dr. Andersson, because there was so little of the bone
exposed. He was sure that they were the vertebrae of a dinosaur but could not spare the time to follow up his hasty investigation. He kept the location in the back of his mind,
however, and as soon as he could, he turned over the task of
collecting these specimens and exploring the district to Dr.
Zdansky.

As soon as the young Austrian scientist visited the area and
began investigating its possibilities, he became very excited.
The section in which the dinosaur deposits were located, in

the general vicinity of a small village named Ning-chia K'ou, was a weird, ugly and most unprepossessing section of badlands; unprepossessing, that is, to any but a scientist in search of geological information. To Dr. Zdansky it was a paleontologist's paradise. He carefully dug out the three vertebrae, which were indeed from the back of a big dinosaur which he could not immediately identify, and then he went on to make some truly exciting discoveries. The rolling, burnt-out hills, composed mostly of sandstone and without vegetation, were not difficult to explore, for there were telltale outcroppings to be seen everywhere. There was no doubt that the whole Meng-yin district had been a vast lake in which strange creatures had cavorted when the world was young. Some evidence of this was to be found in the form of mussels and a variety of other shell deposits almost everywhere Dr. Zdansky scratched the surface. And the outcroppings in the narrow valleys between the rolling folds of hills suggested greater finds to come.

Eagerly, he and his associates, among them Dr. H. C. T'an, a Chinese scientist who had worked with Dr. Andersson for a long time, began an intensified search for significant finds, and it was not long before they discovered a wealth of fossilized bone in the sandstone ledges. As these fossils were exposed, it began to be clear to the scientists that they had discovered a group of dinosaurs entirely unknown up to that time. They also realized that, weird though these badlands seemed then, the whole area must have been much more uncanny when it was a great marsh and lake area peopled by some of the strangest monsters of the Age of Reptiles.

The very first of the fossilized saurian skeletons dug out of the sandstone, and as it turned out the most complete and the prize of the expedition, was that of a giant, long-necked lizard

more than fifteen feet over all, which was imbedded in a
ledge extending rather deep into one of the hillsides. This
presented a real problem for the diggers, for it had to be uncovered with the utmost care to prevent shattering or otherwise injuring the specimens. In fact, every portion as it was
exposed was quickly wrapped with strips of cloth that had
been dipped in gum to protect the bone from the elements
and from accidental fracture.

While the scientists and their workmen were intent on this
very delicate work and paying little attention to anything else
in the vicinity, quite unexpectedly one of the not uncommon
groups of prowling bandits was detected slipping stealthily
down the valley in an effort to surprise and rob them. Ex-
citedly the workmen threw down their tools and started running back to the village. So did the scientists, for they had no
desire to be captured and held for ransom, which was the
favorite custom of Chinese bandits. They gained the village
and were welcomed there by the inhabitants, who were gath-
ering to repel the attack, for it quickly became evident that
the bandits intended to attack the community too. A spirited
fight followed, with many shots fired from behind earth walls
and from doors and windows. But happily, there were no
casualties and the bandits finally withdrew and went back to
the place where Dr. Zdansky's workmen had been digging.

The scientists saw this with sinking hearts, for they were
sure that their precious specimens would be destroyed. Of
course, the bandits were very curious about what the foreign
devils were so interested in back there among the sandstone
ledges. But when, on unwrapping the cloth bandages, they
saw that they covered only fossilized dragons' bones with
which they were all familiar, they left in disgust, and when
Dr. Zdansky and his associates returned to their work, they

found to their relief that only a few of the bandages had been unwrapped and aside from small fragments of bone that had been broken out, their find was uninjured.

Perceiving that they had an almost complete dinosaur skeleton and one very much worth salvaging, they all eagerly turned to the slow, painstaking work of cutting away the part of the sandstone ledge in which the fossil was imbedded. Because the skeleton was so large, this had to be done in sections of a size that could be easily handled by a small group of men and that could be numbered and later fitted together to form the perfect skeleton. This took days, and when it was finally finished, Dr. Zdansky was faced with the difficult task of transporting the heavy sandstone chunks, as well as their many other specimens, to the nearest railroad. To guard against breakage, each chunk of sandstone was first wrapped, then packed in straw and crated in an ironbound case. This finally had to be moved out of the hill country mostly in pushcarts powered by peasant labor, for a survey of the whole area did not produce a single available domestic animal for draught work.

But they managed to get their cumbersome load out and ship it back to Peking, where Dr. Andersson took charge of it and later shipped it to Sweden and Dr. Wiman at Upsala University. Meanwhile, Dr. Zdansky and his associate, Dr. T'an, went back to searching for more specimens. They found another, somewhat less complete, skeleton of this same long-necked saurian and part of one of the ugliest and most unbelievable of the giant reptiles, a stegosaurus, the great lizard with the homely visage, little head and armor-plated back. It had a powerful ten-foot tail equipped with foot-long spikes, a deadly weapon just right for lashing its enemies to death. The two scientists, in addition, brought back a wealth of other fossil material, all of which added tremendously to the scientific knowledge of early Asia.

In the meantime, back in Sweden, Dr. Wiman was carefully chipping away all the sandstone that surrounded the first complete skeleton and assembling it for study. It was he who finally decided that Dr. Zdansky had discovered a member of an entirely new and rather amazing family of dinosaurs which he chose to call *Helopodidae* of the species *Helopus Zdanski,* thus, as is customary, naming it after its discoverer, Dr. Zdansky.

The Swedish professor established the fact that it was an amphibious creature which probably spent more time in the water than on the land. It was a comparatively short-legged saurian with a very long neck, small head, and long tail. The feet were broad and flat on the bottom, resembling in many respects the feet of creatures who spend much of their time on marshy ground. This clue and the evident fact that the dinosaur's bone ends had been well cushioned with cartilage and that there were air spaces in the vertebrae, suggested to Dr. Wiman that the dinosaur was especially equipped by nature to spend most of its time in the water.

Added to this, Dr. Wiman pointed out that the pelvic structure and the leg bones were heavy and solid and acted like the weighted feet of a diver. This and the broad feet made it quite clear that the creature actually walked on the soft lake bottom and fed on underwater vegetation. Its long neck and small head with nostrils, eyes and ears set high in effect became a combination periscope and snorkle which would permit the monster to wander around over the lake bottom, raising only its snaky neck and head just above the surface of the water to breathe and to look and listen for signs of danger. It was the broad feet that suggested the name *Helopus* (marsh foot) to Dr. Wiman.

And Dr. H. C. T'an, working with Dr. Zdansky, discovered another lake-dwelling type of dinosaur which was later named *Tanius sinensis* in his honor. It was almost a perfect specimen and it was discovered at Chiang Chun Ting. T'an undertook to dig it out of the sandstone, but was only able partially to complete the task. Dr. Zdansky returned at a later date and excavated the rest of the skeleton for him. It was of a long-necked, heavy-bodied saurian build, much after the fashion of a kangaroo, with thick, stumpy tail and heavy hind legs equipped with feet composed of three broad toes. Unlike the *Helopus,* the *Tanius* had a large head and powerful jaws equipped with strong grinders for teeth.

About the same time that Dr. Zdansky and his confrere, Dr. T'an, were making their interesting discoveries in the Meng-Yin district of Shantung, the fossilized remains of equally strange and hitherto unknown dinosaurs were turning up in other sections of Asia, any one or all of which could well have been considered dragons by credulous peasants who might have found their bones. During the summer of 1922, what has been looked upon by scientists as the most outstanding series of scientific expeditions ever undertaken in Asia were started by the American Museum of Natural History. Under the leadership of Dr. Roy Chapman Andrews, the first expedition was to explore the Gobi desert region of Mongolia. The newspapers in America dubbed them the "Missing Link Expeditions" because word got out before the scientists left New York that they hoped, among other things, to find evidences of primitive man in the Gobi area.

Dr. Henry Fairfield Osborn, then president of the American Museum of Natural History, had long held the opinion that Asia was the cradle of mankind and that someday revealing relics of the creature who ultimately became modern man would be found on that continent. Dr. Osborn was right. The fossilized bones of primitive man were found in Asia, but the American Museum expedition did not find them. Instead they found dinosaurs that laid eggs and other dinosaurs that were believed to live by robbing the nests and eating the eggs of the saurians that laid them, as well as many other forms of the great prehistoric lizards.

During the first summer that the expedition was in Asia, one of the members found a reptilian skull that was not immediately identified. It was sent back to Dr. Osborn in New York for examination. It did not take long for the great scientist to recognize it as the skull of an early ancestor of a group of dinosaurs known as the *Ceretopsians*. They were huge horned dinosaurs, and fossilized bones of these reptiles had already been found in America. The discovery of their early ancestors in Asia suggested that the huge creatures had, like man himself, migrated by way of a land bridge from Asia to North America around a hundred million years before. Dr. Osborn cabled Dr. Andrews that he had made a great discovery and that the expedition should return to the area of the Gobi desert, where the skull had been found, as early as possible for a really intensive search for more dinosaur treasure. The scientist named the creature *Protoceratops Andrewsi* after the leader of the expedition.

The explorers had called the area of the find Flaming Cliffs, and the next spring, when conditions permitted field work in the desert country, arrangements were made to return there. It was a tremendously difficult trek of more than four hundred miles across a waterless desert waste that was parched and burnt out and made more stark by the bleached bones of camels, sheep and horses that had failed to reach their destination. Although the main part of the expedition traveled in motor cars, the gasoline had to be brought through by camel train, and it was a very grave concern of everyone from Dr. Andrews down to the humblest camel driver whether enough animals could survive the trip to carry sufficient gasoline to get the cars and their occupants to a place of safety, once they got that far out in the desert.

The area in which the dinosaur skull was found proved to be hot, dry, waterless desert, where no one would care to remain any longer than necessary. So as soon as camp was pitched, every member of the expedition began an intensive search for fossilized bones, and with amazing results. Almost immediately all sorts of saurian fossils began to turn up everywhere. Skulls and bones of a number of the giant lizards of the Age of Reptiles were found in every gully and washout explored. Then, to cap the climax of an almost unbelievable adventure in fossil hunting, on the second day of their search of the area, one of the members of the party, a scientist named George Olsen, reported that he believed he had found some fossilized dinosaur eggs, and that he had left them undisturbed so that everyone could see exactly how they appeared *in situ*. He urged everyone to follow him into the gully he had been exploring.

At first all the members of the party had a feeling that they were being spoofed, but then it began to dawn on them that no one knew exactly how the saurians were born. So presently there was a rush to follow Olsen to his place of discovery. This proved to be an area below a sandstone ledge where, in plain sight, lay three objects that were very obviously fossilized eggs. They had been imbedded in the sandstone but had broken away. The round, smooth ends of two others were still to be seen protruding from the bank, and there were the molds and broken fragments of more eggs also imbedded in the soft sandstone slope.

But the big surprise was yet to come, for as Olsen began to dig out some of the eggs and egg fragments, he exposed what proved to be the skeleton of a small dinosaur only about four feet long in the sandstone just above the eggs. It looked for all the world as if this creature had been in the very act of robbing a dinosaur nest of its eggs when a terrific sandstorm had swept across the great wasteland area, swiftly covering the saurian and the nest it was robbing under tremendous quantities of sand, thus embalming and burying the tableau for millions of years. Dr. Osborn, when he examined the skeleton, later verified the fact that this reptilian thief was probably a creature that lived on the eggs of other dinosaurs. It was toothless and equipped with adequate digging apparatus to be a nest robber. He named it *Oviraptor,* the egg seizer.

That first group of dinosaur eggs was by no means the last to be discovered. After Olsen had made his find and the strange, elongated eggs had been thoroughly examined, a concentrated search was started to locate more. They began to turn up in a number of places in that hot, glaring, burnt-out area of badlands. Some were discovered exposed on the surface, and others were revealed imbedded in the sandstone. Some were broken to expose fossilized embryonic dinosaurs inside. It was possible to trace the tiny bones of what would have been ugly, armor-covered baby lizards. The eggs themselves, which were probably those of a *Protoceratops,* were not as large as one would expect a dinosaur's eggs to be. They measured about eight inches in length and in many respects they were quite different from the familiar eggs of turtles, snakes, and those of our present-day birds.

The discovery of dinosaur eggs was an outstanding achievement for Dr. Andrews and his expedition, for up to that time no scientific group or individual had come across any of the curious objects that Olsen had unearthed. In speaking of them later, Dr. Andrews said that he and all the members of his party were completely surprised at the discovery.

"No one really knew whether dinosaurs laid eggs," said he, "because in no dinosaur deposits had any been found. But dinosaurs were reptiles, and most reptiles lay eggs, so it would not be unlikely that dinosaurs laid eggs also. But we had not thought of looking for them when we went into the Gobi. Neither did we expect to discover dinosaur fossils, for up to that time no dinosaurs had been found in Asia north of the Himalaya Mountains."

But the dinosaur eggs, of which more than two dozen were found, were by no means the only accomplishments of this search of the Gobi desert area. The diligent American paleontologists made many historic finds, not the least of which was a treasure house of scrambled dinosaur remains. Literally hundreds of great saurians, both of the carnivorous and the herbivorous type, were in some way trapped in a marshy bay of what had once been a big lake. There they had expired, and their remains, when the flesh had rotted away, had become entombed in the mud and ultimately petrified as the lake dried up and became a desert. Dr. Andrews describes it in his book, *Under a Lucky Star,* as a quarry of dinosaur bones, and such a place could have been the source of dragons' bones for all of China for centuries had it been accessible to the bone diggers.

The Discovery
of Peking Man
3

It was a villager's natural interest in anyone digging for dragons' bones (he dug them himself as did most of his neighbors) and the advice he gave Dr. Andersson that led to the cave at Chou-k'ou Tien, where ultimately the fossil remains of the most primitive man then known to science were brought to light. Savants named him "Peking man," and for nearly two decades relics of this hominid held the stage of scientific interest in the origin of mankind, only to disappear quite suddenly. And now, unless the Communist archeologists can shed some light on the whereabouts of many wooden cases of his invaluable fossil remains, which they apparently are unable to do, his fate will probably continue to be a complete mystery.

Dr. Andersson, as general director of the Geological Survey of China, learned of a quarry in a place called Chicken Bone Hill in Chou-k'ou Tien where fossilized bones could be found in the red clay that filled the fissures in the limestone. In fact, he went there several times himself as early as 1917 to do some digging. But he was always disappointed because the bones brought to light were those of birds and rodents and for the most part seemed to belong to creatures of a comparatively recent period. But it was an attractive and interesting section of the country and not too far from Peking, and he always felt an urge to return to the area. (See Map 1.)

So, when Dr. Zdansky came to China on his two-year leave of absence from Upsala University in Sweden, Dr. Andersson planned to take him to Chou-k'ou Tien if for no other purpose than to show him the country. But both became so busy and so involved in exploration work in other areas that it was more than a year before the promised visit to the lime quarry country took place. It was finally inspired by the arrival in China of Dr. Walter Granger, long-time friend and one of the scientists who joined the American Museum of Natural History's Central Asiatic Expedition under the leadership of Dr. Roy Chapman Andrews.

Dr. Andersson thought it would be a friendly act to introduce Dr. Granger to fossil hunting in China by taking him out to Chicken Bone Hill and at the same time show Dr. Zdansky the limestone quarry country and give him an opportunity to do some digging in a place in which Dr. Andersson felt there were always great possibilities of making discoveries of more than ordinary significance. The caves in the limestone country always intrigued him, and he had a feeling that someday someone would turn up crude stone tools or other evidence of primitive man in one of the caves.

It was a not unpleasant trip from Peking for the three of them and when they got off the train at the little village of Lao-niu Kou, the valley and the mountains that closed it in made a picture just as attractive as Dr. Andersson remembered it.

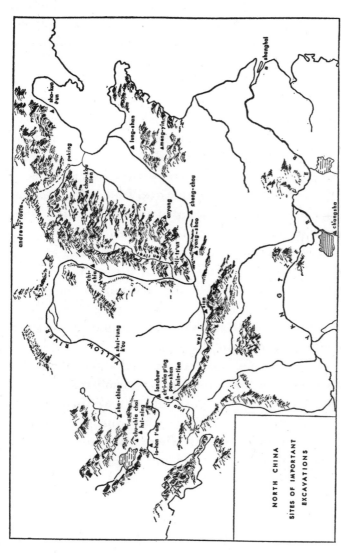

Map No. 1, showing the location of Chou-k'ou Tien, Anyang and the route taken to the Gobi desert by Dr. Roy Chapman Andrews. Here also are located the sites of some of the more important digs in North China.

In the still September evening, with the sun dropping low behind the hills, the shadows were creeping slowly across the valley. Thin strands of blue cooking smoke had begun to climb up into the cooling evening air. Over toward the jagged, hard-looking ledges and outcroppings of limestone pitted by gaping quarry holes now in shadow came faintly and at irregular intervals a thin squeaking and creaking as the small blue-clad figure of a quarry oxcart-driver and his span made their way down the dusty road toward the village. He and his heavy wheeled vehicle appeared and disappeared as the low, barren hills intermittently hid the road from sight. Beyond the quarries the bald hills mounted up behind each other against the blue, cloudless sky. They looked smooth from a distance because the tortuous creases between them and the sudden jagged outcroppings on their flanks were hidden from the viewers. So, too, were the beehive kilns of the lime burners spotted haphazardly among the hills, their presence revealed only by smudges of smoke mounting upward, to vanish against the deep blue of the heavens.

In another direction, out of sight beyond a spur of angular outcroppings of stone, Dr. Andersson remembered the location of the somewhat shabby enclosure of the Yün-feng temple, where he had lived for a little while during a previous visit to the area. It belonged just where it was, for its history was bound tightly to those scarred and bare little mountains whose frequent ledges of slate had afforded men a way of earning their meager living for more than a thousand years. Many centuries past, when Yün-feng was a center of devout and learned Buddhism, the abbot (whether more to store up grace in heaven than to preserve the sacred text unchanged, no one will ever know) noticed the fine large slates that were taken from the quarries in the hills and decided to commission stonecutters to inscribe on them the characters of the sacred texts. How many decades the work went on is unknown, but in 1957 the mainland government (which is to say, the Communists) announced the discovery of thousands of these slate tablets, two by four feet in size, buried under masonry walls and hidden in many of the numerous limestone caves which made the area a dwelling site for prehistoric Chinese from the dawn of man's time on earth.

Beyond the village itself, with its house walls of dusty pastels and grimy white—with its roofs of slate for the great houses and thatch for the lowly—could be seen for miles on miles through the dust haze, the long, flat, mighty and fertile north China plain. The house shapes in the village, with their sharp eaves and higgledy-piggledy arrangement, were in marked contrast to the vista of neat, geometrically arranged fields of wheat, maize and soybean. And to complete the picture, as the visiting scientists took in the scene, coming at a rhythmic trot along the dykelike path that separated one family's field from another, was a tiny figure with a long carrying-pole over his shoulder and two large wooden pails suspended from it. Even from a distance it was evident the pails were empty because of the way they dangled and danced with abandon as they swayed to the rhythm of his jogging step. The peasant had already spread the night soil on his crop and was returning after his last chore for the day. The silent pleasure reflected in the smiles of his two guests satisfied Dr. Andersson that he had brought them to quite the proper place to give them a pleasant picture of China and to introduce Dr. Granger to the engaging archeological occupation of digging for dragons' bones.

The most prolific source of fossils in the quarry at Chicken Bone Hill was a great pillar of red clay that stood alone on the floor of the quarry pit. Dr. Andersson realized that at some time or other this clay had filled a big cavity in the solid limestone, but lime burners and quarry men had carefully broken away all the stone without disturbing the clay. He learned that there was a superstitious fear behind this. The cave that the clay had filled had been the place where a number of foxes lived. These thievish creatures had stolen so many chickens in the Chou-k'ou Tien area that the curses of the people had changed them into evil spirits. But the foxes had their revenge. There were stories about men who had gone mad while digging dragons' bones from the clay that had filled the cave, and the peasants said that the evil spirit-foxes were responsible.

While the three scientists were carefully digging out some small bones from the clay, a man of the neighborhood stood watching them curiously, if not, indeed, fearfully. But when nothing untoward happened to them, the peasant grew bolder and began to ask about their reason for digging dragons' bones, which to him they were obviously doing. Dr. Andersson explained their interest in fossilized bones, and suddenly the man confided to them that they were wasting their time there and that he knew a place where they could get much bigger and better dragons' bones.

The scientists were immediately curious, and Dr. Andersson began to question the peasant. With the proper encouragement, the native told them of another abandoned quarry not so very far away. He suggested that they pack their equipment and follow him over some low limestone hills. This they did and shortly reached a quarry hole dug out of the hill, with an almost perpendicular limestone wall at the back. In this there was what had once been a rather large fissure—so large, in fact, as to form a cave. This was also filled with red clay, and inspection revealed to the scientists that it was a treasury of fossils. In a few minutes they found several excellent specimens of the jawbones of larger animals, and all three of them began to feel that they were on the verge of making some remarkable discoveries.

Next day they returned to the quarry and proceeded methodically to uncover specimens and wrap them for protection and preservation. Dr. Andersson said that the harvest exceeded their most hopeful expectations. The red clay yielded the jaws with teeth intact of several prehistoric stags, as well as the teeth of several rhinoceri, the jaws of a hyena and portions of jawbone that came from the great cave bear. And there was evidence that there was much, much more to be found in that clay pit, for it apparently extended inward and downward into what had definitely been a large cave.

A heavy rainstorm and washout made digging impossible for several days after their first efforts, and as a result neither Dr. Andersson nor Dr. Granger was able to do any further work at the cave, for they had to return to Peking as soon as they were able to travel. But Dr. Zdansky remained at the Chou-k'ou Tien deposits and in the course of several weeks he turned up some exciting material in the form of fossilized bones, as well as some interesting flakes of quartz.

Dr. Andersson, who made several trips out to the cave while Dr. Zdansky was at work, was immediately attracted by these quartz flakes, which he perceived were sharp and rudely shaped in a form that would make them convenient cutting instruments. In fact, the more he studied them, the more he became convinced that, though they might have flaked off of any of the quartz veins that streaked the limestone, they had actually been used by human beings as rude knives for one purpose or another. In writing of this later, Dr. Andersson

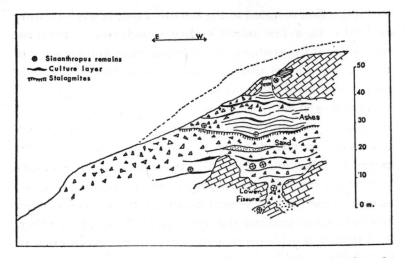

Sketch of cross section of cave at Chou-k'ou Tien showing the location of the human remains that later became known as Sinanthropus Pekinensis, *more popularly referred to as Peking Man. (Redrawn from Teilhard de Chardin,* Fossil Men)

said that he had a very much stronger presentiment that the deposits in this cave held archeological secrets that were of tremendous scientific value, not the least of which was definite evidence of the fact that the cave had been occupied by prehistoric man. He told this to Dr. Zdansky and said that he was sure the Austrian scientist would turn up some actual remains of human ancestors if he pursued his search diligently and got to the very bottom of the cave. It was a true prediction, but he did not realize the tremendous amount of material that would have to be emptied out of the cave before the treasures they were after would actually be found.

Dr. Zdansky continued to make interesting fossil discoveries as he dug deeper into the clay deposit. But as his work progressed, it became more difficult and dangerous because his workmen were undercutting heavy, overhanging walls in many places. Soon it became evident that the work was reaching a point where shoring by means of heavy scaffolding was necessary to prevent a disastrous cave-in. And since neither money nor material was available for this, the digging was finally discontinued.

However, Dr. Andersson could never completely forget the feeling he had had that somewhere in that cave was to be found important evidence that it had been the abode of early man, and he tried very hard to make it possible for Dr. Zdansky to get back to Chou-k'ou Tien and resume work there. Through these efforts the Austrian scientist did go back to the cave and carry on his excavating intermittently. With exciting results, too, for he turned up the fossil remains of a number of prehistoric creatures, including the saber-toothed tiger, the cave lion, the cave bear, and bones of the rhinoceros, horse, pig, deer, buffalo, and ape.

Because the work was being carried on through the generosity of Swedish financing and with the blessing of Uppsala University in Stockholm, much of the material removed from the cave was being shipped to Sweden for study by Dr. Zdansky's superior, Dr. Wiman, and it was from there that Dr. Andersson got word they had found the first hominid remains: two teeth, or, rather, one molar and one premolar from an infant.

Dr. Andersson was tremendously thrilled by this information. His long-held belief that evidence of early man would be found in the cave was justified. Eagerly he secured photographs of the teeth from Sweden and had them made into lantern slides to illustrate a lecture given at the Peking Medical School in honor of the visiting Crown Prince of Sweden, who was an enthusiastic amateur archeologist himself. The lecture announced to the world the finding of the first evidence of prehistoric man on the Asiatic continent, and was pronounced one of the most important results of the extensive archeological work done in China under Swedish direction. The Swedish scientist also suggested that further investigation on a much larger and more costly scale be done at the Chou-k'ou Tien cave by the Geological Survey of China and the Peking Union Medical School, financed by funds which Dr. Andersson felt certain could be obtained from the Rockefeller Foundation.

But aside from the Swedish Crown Prince and the world of science, particularly the Chinese and foreign scientists working in China, the discovery of two teeth, which Dr. Zdansky labeled *Homo Sp?,* did not create any earth-shaking reaction. The newspapers did not pick it up and feature it and not a great deal of publicity was given to the find even in the field of science. In truth, there were some scholars who were extremely skeptical about the teeth being human. A French scholar and friend of Dr. Andersson wrote and warned him that it would be easy to make a mistake. The tooth and premolar could be from some carnivore, he insisted. He cautioned Dr. Andersson not to be too hopeful of their human character until more and better specimens turned up.

Fortunately, representatives of the Rockefeller Foundation were not deterred by these doubts, and through the efforts of Dr. Andersson and a Canadian physician and anatomist, Dr. Davidson Black of Peking medical school, they were persuaded to finance further exploration of the Chou-k'ou Tien cave under the auspices of the Chinese Geological Survey. All the material removed from the cave was to become the property of the Geological Survey, but it was to be studied, evaluated and described by Dr. Black. Arrangements were made to bring Dr. Birger Bohlin, a Swedish scientist who had worked with Dr. Zdansky and Dr. Wiman at Uppsala, to China to direct the excavation work, since Dr. Zdansky's leave had expired and he had to return to Sweden. The whole project was placed under a Chinese scientist, Dr. Ting. Dr. C. Li was appointed as geologist who was to be responsible for geological and topographical observations.

China was far from a pleasant or indeed a safe place for foreigners in 1927, and in April, when the work at Chou-k'ou Tien was started again, war was raging in a number of different places, sometimes so close to the cave in which Dr. Bohlin and his crew were digging that they could hear the sounds of battle. All too often there were troop movements in the vicinity and Dr. Bohlin said that now and again battle-happy bandits would find it humorous to lob a hand grenade into the quarry hole perilously close to the entrance of the cave and scare the wits out of the coolie laborers.

A slowly growing hatred of westerners was again appearing in China, where seeds of nationalism were beginning to develop, and the Chinese began pillaging and looting the establishments of English and Americans. Foreigners were being kidnapped and held for ransom, and quite a few disappeared completely, never to be heard from again. There were serious riots in Nanking, Hong Kong, and Shanghai, and conditions became so bad that a number of western nations, particularly the British, rushed warships to several Chinese ports to protect their nationals.

Dr. Bohlin was aware that his life was endangered daily by this antiforeign feeling, but he refused to let that make any difference in his work of exploring the cave. With a larger labor force available now, the cave was very thoroughly opened up, though not, of course, emptied. It was found to be larger than anyone had anticipated: it extended more than one hundred sixty feet into the limestone and was more than fifty feet in width. The clay and other deposits filling it were estimated to be as much as sixty feet deep in places.

Excavating in a scientific manner with everything being thoroughly examined and evaluated is necessarily slow and painstaking work. For that reason, while Dr. Bohlin and his crew labored unremittingly for almost five months, only about 3,000 cubic yards of the deposit in the cave were brought out and scrutinized before approaching winter weather and precarious local conditions made it advisable to stop the operations in mid-October. A number of highly interesting and scientifically valuable fossil remains of animals were brought to light, but it was not until three days before the work was to stop that the first and only evidence of human occupancy of the cave found during that particular dig turned up. Dr. Bohlin himself found another hominid tooth, and he was delighted. Indeed, he considered this a satisfactory reward for the months he had spent grubbing in the red clay in the cave.

Filled with elation, he personally carried the tooth to Peking when the work was finished and the laborers were paid off and dismissed. But getting back to the capital was in itself a very dangerous journey. Though the distance was less than fifty miles, the Swedish scientist had to travel through country bristling with bandit soldiers and warlord troops who had built up a special hatred for westerners. The wonder was that Dr. Bohlin was able to talk his way out of several difficult situations into which he inadvertently blundered before he finally managed to get inside the city.

So enthusiastic was he over this tiny treasure he carefully carried in his pocket that he did not stop at his home. Instead, he went directly to the Medical School, where he found Dr. Black in his laboratory and delivered the tooth to him. At the same time he assured the anatomist that there would un-questionably be more evidence of early man forthcoming when digging was resumed.

But for Dr. Black no further evidence was needed to help him establish the fact that the creatures to whom this molar and those unearthed by Dr. Zdansky belonged were definitely human in character. And after searching study and careful comparisons were made with other teeth, ranging from those of man to those of apes, Dr. Black decided that Dr. Bohlin's find was from a hominid (in this instance, actually a child) distinctive enough to deserve the designation of a new genus. In his scientific paper about the work he labeled it *Sinan-thropus Pekinensis,* in keeping with the usual procedure. Thus did this lowly cave creature of more than a half million years ago become immortalized as one of the earliest an-cestors of present-day man and the first to be discovered in Asia.

It will be recalled here that one of the objectives of the Central Asiatic Expedition, under the direction of Dr. Roy Chapman Andrews of the American Museum of Natural History, was to discover evidence of primitive man in Asia. Headquarters for the expedition were set up in Peking, and part of Dr. Andrews' plan was to explore areas of the western hills where the Chou-k'ou Tien cave was located. Unfortu-nately, the Americans were prevented from doing this because of a request made by the Chinese Geological Survey that they refrain from working in that area out of courtesy to the Survey's interest in the project being carried on there. If it had not been for that request, it is possible that the American scientists might have had the distinction of discovering the

Peking man. Dr. Andrews was in Peking a number of times during the years in which the Chou-k'ou Tien deposits were being explored and, being a personal friend of Dr. Davidson Black, he was able to follow his work very closely right up to the time of Dr. Black's unfortunate death and the development of full-scale war in China, which made it necessary for foreign scientists to leave the country.

But if that ugly little discolored tooth excited Dr. Black and the other scientists when Dr. Bohlin delivered it to him, how much more must they have been thrilled by the later discoveries in the cave at Chou-k'ou Tien. The work was resumed the following year and Dr. Bohlin's assistants were paleontologists Dr. C. C. Young (Yang Chung-chien) and a Dr. W. C. P'ei (P'ei Wen-chung) who was destined at a later date to make the most spectacular find to come out of Chou-k'ou Tien before the Communists dropped the bamboo curtain on all of China.

Almost from the beginning of the work in 1928 what amounted to spectacular finds (in the eyes of the scientists) began to make their appearance. Teeth turned up quite regularly, then portions of skulls of both children and adults, and shortly a section of an adult human's jaw appeared. It contained several teeth and was in excellent shape for study by the scientists. Later, other jaw sections were found, including a portion of a child's chin, which permitted a comparison between the chin of a modern Chinese child and the chins of a young chimpanzee and of a child of the latest Stone Age in China. The result of this comparison and others made by Dr. Black proved beyond a doubt that *Sinanthropus*, in spite of some apelike characteristics, was definitely a human being belonging somewhere between modern man and the apes, but with a larger brain than those arboreal creatures.

If, however, the discoveries of 1928 at Chou-k'ou Tien excited a limited scientific world, the finds of the following year must have produced a reaction akin to jubilation among archeologists and paleontologists everywhere. Dr. Bohlin accepted an assignment to join another expedition going to Chinese Turkestan, and his assistant, Dr. W. C. P'ei, was put in charge of exploring the cave further, with a big crew at his disposal and adequate funds still being supplied by the Rockefeller Foundation.

The digging was hampered at first because of heavy rainfall, but it was possible to do quite a lot of preliminary work and establish the approximate size of the cave, along with the fact that at some time in the distant past the domed roof had collapsed and fallen in. The floor of the cave had not been located because the bottom of the deposit had never been reached, so after the rainy season was over and digging could be started again, Dr. P'ei had his crew work on the task of penetrating to the lowest level. When they had got down about sixty feet, it suddenly developed that there were two smaller caves. With a lot of digging, one could be worked into horizontally, but the other could be entered only by climbing down on a rope.

Dr. P'ei decided to explore the one that could be entered most easily, and work proceeded by removing the deposit from the horizontal gallery, which soon revealed that it had very probably been a dwelling cave. They began to find flakes of quartz that had undoubtedly been used as cutting tools. Some of these bore indications that rude attempts had been made to shape them for easier handling. Stones were unearthed that were not to be found locally, and there was evidence that whoever had occupied the cave had known how to use fire. There were strata of deposits that later were determined to be ashes of many cooking fires mixed with pieces of charred wood and burnt bone. There were bones, too, of large animals, such as the rhinoceros, which the cave dwellers had unquestionably killed and cooked for food.

One afternoon Dr. P'ei and his men were carefully digging out the deposits in the gallery when quite unexpectedly he revealed evidence of what promised to be a thrilling find. He exposed the curved structure of something which, when completely excavated, proved to be the fossilized skull of *Sinanthropus Pekinensis* himself. Fortunately, it was buried almost entirely in sand and thus was easily exhumed. A portion of it, however, was encased in travertine, and a rather large block of that hard limestone had to be removed in order to handle the skull and bring it to the surface. Dr. P'ei was elated, of course. So was everyone associated with the dig. Word was sent to all the scientists in Peking who had anything to do with the expedition, and telegrams were dispatched to Dr. Black and Dr. Andersson telling them the good news.

Several days later Dr. P'ei personally took the skull, carefully wrapped and well protected, to the Medical School in Peking and turned it over to Dr. Black. He immediately began work at the very delicate and painstaking task of removing the stone that enclosed the back portion of the skull, an achievement that consumed almost four months of his time. Using dentist drills, he managed to remove the fossilized bones and save even the endocast of the skull. Meanwhile, there were a number of scientists in Peking at the time of the discovery and word spread very fast that the skull had been found and was in the possession of Dr. Black. As soon as they could, they hurried to Dr. Black's laboratory to have a chance to look at this tremendously interesting specimen of modern man's cave ancestor.

The skull was that of a young man and, aside from the facial structure, which was missing, was remarkably complete. Later during 1928 two more incomplete skulls were found in fragmentary form, and somewhat later, in 1932, a very large portion of the skull of what was presumed to be a cave woman was found. These crania, with the mass of accompanying material that was taken out of the deposits, represented the finest collection of material on primitive man available up to that time for scientific scrutiny and, of course, distinguished scholars immediately became interested in the collection and data being developed and studied by Dr. Black for the Chinese Geological Survey.

Dr. Andersson, who had the distinction of discovering the Chou-k'ou Tien site and promoting exploration there, and who made the uncanny prediction that the remains of primitive man would be found in the cave, was at all times very close to Dr. Black and his studies of the material. Later in his book, Dr. Andersson wrote that our knowledge of the early history of the human race was immeasurably advanced by the study of these skulls.

No other site before 1928 had yielded so much in the way of valuable material for the study of the beginning of the human race as the cave at Chou-k'ou Tien. Nor did any other place hold such promise of future revelations. In an effort to preserve the cave in the quarry and the surrounding area as a source of further information and to prevent it from being disturbed by untrained villagers in their search for dragons' bones, the site was finally purchased by the Chinese Geological Survey.

The scientific world, and of course the Chinese Government in particular, decided that the exploration work should continue to be carried on and every effort made to capitalize on the world-wide interest in Peking man. So in spite of the spreading hostilities and the continued threats of Japanese aggression, work was resumed in 1929 and continued for several years under an especially organized department of the Chinese Geological Survey, known as the Cenozoic Research Laboratory. The work continued to be financed by the Rockefeller Foundation, and Dr. Black was in charge of the preparation and study of the tremendous amount of material that came out of the area.

Indeed, it is believed that Dr. Black in his sheer enthusiasm to get through the hundreds of cases of material that had been moved from the limestone quarry to his laboratory literally worked himself to death. Unhappily, he died in 1934 and with his passing, for a time, the investigation seemed to have lost its incentive. But the following year, with much remaining to be done, Dr. Franz Weidenreich, a German anatomist of wide reputation, was asked to take over the work left by Dr. Black. The invitation was extended by the Rockefeller Foundation, with the approval of the Chinese Geological Survey, and Dr. Weidenreich made remarkable progress in developing casts of the Peking man material and evaluating it.

Conditions in China were deteriorating fast. But even after Japanese troops invaded Manchuria, the German anatomist remained in Peking, in spite of constant harassment by the invaders, and continued his work. In fact, he stayed until it became all too evident that to remain longer would be dangerous. Only then did he leave for America, where he joined the staff of the American Museum of Natural History in New York. Happily, he had been able, after considerable effort, to get the series of casts he had made of the Peking man material out of the country with him, never realizing then that these casts might one day be all that could be considered material evidence of the discovery of *Sinanthropus Pekinensis.*

When conditions became so chaotic in Peking that scientific work was next to impossible and Dr. Weidenreich had left the country, the Chinese Government attempted to save the numerous cases of Peking man material by turning them over to the custody of the Marine guard at the U.S. Legation, in the hope that they could be shipped to America safely. But about that time the Japanese were moving in fast and the U.S. Marine guards were made prisoner while their baggage, and presumably the cases containing the remains of Peking man, were all confiscated. And it was right at that point that *Sinanthropus Pekinensis* disappeared completely, nor has anything been seen or heard of his scientific relics since.

Embarrassed by the fact that they were the last to have charge of the cases containing the fossils of this first prehistoric man of Asia, the Marine Corps conducted a systematic search for the missing cases in China and Japan and many of the islands after the war in the Pacific was ended. They detailed an officer, Second Lieutenant Lucian W. Pye, who had been born and brought up in north China and spoke the language fluently, to find them, and he devoted a lot of time to the task, but to no avail. No trace of the cases has ever been found since the day in 1941 when they were presumably put on a train for Tientsin by the Japanese.

"My own theory," says former Lieutenant, now Professor Lucian Pye, "is that when the Marines guarding the boxes were picked up by the Japanese troops on December 8, 1941, they probably got separated from these interesting-looking green painted cases. When they got the chance, the *chiao-hangs,* the porters, took them and broke them open. They wanted the wood and excelsior in them. Fuel is valuable in north China. Maybe a couple of them were clever enough to see the value to the Chinese druggists of the dragon bones and teeth in them and sold the scientific treasures for a few coppers. Who knows?"

At any rate, the search for the missing relics of *Sinanthropus Pekinensis* has been abandoned.

It is interesting to know, however (before closing this chapter on Peking man), that in 1957 Dr. P'ei Wen-chung, still working for the Cenozoic Research Laboratory, under the direction of the Communists, of course, found pieces of quartz and flint which he believed to be stone tools not unlike some of those that he found in the cave in Chou-k'ou Tien back in 1930. These, he thought, might well mark the site of what could be another *Sinanthropus* find.

The scientist made his discovery along a footpath leading to the tiny settlement known as Li-ts'un (One Mile Village). At the bottom of a badlands formation, where it joins the wheat fields, was discovered a pocket of loose sand and gravel which had been overlaid by almost twenty-five feet of shale made up partly of compressed peat. This had obviously been the bottom of a prehistoric lake for tens of thousands of years. But before that lake had even formed, perhaps a hundred thousand years ago, there had been mammalian creatures of the Cenozoic Age, hyenas, rhinoceri, and a very early cowlike animal known as the *Bos primigenius*, which had walked over this sandy pocket, and their fossilized, fragmented bones still lay there. Most important, perhaps they were the prey of Paleolithic man.

The chipped and battered stones investigated by Dr. P'ei seem definitely, according to his report to the Ministry of Culture, to have been chipped and fractured in the manner of Paleolithic implements. Dr. P'ei says that certain spots on these stones are caused by blows of pointed stones while the worked stone was being held against a rock used as an anvil. He and his colleagues (including Mr. Chia Lan-po, who headed the first survey of the area and wrote the report with Dr. P'ei) feel certain that these stones are rude implements of early man. This site and the nearby village of Ting-ts'un are the only areas aside from Chou-k'ou Tien where traces of Paleolithic man have been reported.

Author's Note—Shortly after this manuscript was finished information reached this country by way of the Communist scientific press and Dr. Kwang-chih Chang, Chinese scholar and instructor in anthropology on the faculty of Yale University, that fossil evidence of at least six different humanoids have been uncovered by Communist explorers. These fossils, mostly teeth, it is believed, are said to help in a small way to bridge the vast gap in the Pleistocene age (a million years, more or less) between *Sinanthropus,* as represented by Peking Man, and Modern Man, according to *Science Service* in which a story of Dr. Chang's report was published.

Successor   4

to *Sinanthropus*

About the time, or shortly thereafter, that Dr. Andersson and his associates, Drs. Zdansky and Granger, encouraged by the discovery of flints that revealed human handicraft, were digging into the deposits in the cave at Chou-k'ou Tien for more evidence of men of the Old Stone Age, two other scientists were pursuing a similar quest on the southern edge of the Ordos desert on the border of Suiyuan Province. They were French Jesuit priests, Father Emil Licent and Father Tielhard de Chardin, the latter professor of paleontology at the Institut Catholique in Paris.

Father Licent, like Dr. Andersson, had been collecting and investigating in Northern China and the Yellow River District for quite a few years when in 1920, again like Dr. Andersson, he discovered flints bearing evidence of having been shaped, albeit crudely, by human ingenuity. He made his discovery at the bottom of the loess deposit at Ching-yan Fu in Eastern Kansu Province.

Immediately he became inspired to search for further evidence of men of the Old Stone Age. It was not until two years later, however, after investigating many rumors and following many leads, that he located culture deposits at Shui-tung K'ou (see Map 1) which gave real promise of important discovery. Here were more flints and quartz fragments that showed evidence of human efforts to shape them, along with ashes from cooking fires and other assurances that he had really found an ancient dwelling site.

So important did all this seem to Father Licent that he decided to get in touch with his friend, the professor of paleontology, Father de Chardin. The information of his discovery was so convincing to the professor from Paris that he agreed to work with Father Licent, and as soon as possible they joined forces at Shui-tung K'ou. What Father de Chardin found made him just as enthusiastic as his confrere, for when the workmen under their careful direction removed the loess deposit down to a depth of forty feet, they encountered signs of what had once been a dwelling site of people of the Old Stone Age.

The area of the site was rather extensive but plainly marked not only with evidence of cooking fires, but with pieces of bones, which were the obvious remnants of meals. An amazing collection of stone fragments as well as completed stone tools were also found, all of which suggested that there had been a number of artisans at this home site. Among the discoveries were scrapers, drills, flint points, stone knife blades and other rude implements, all easily identified and composing a very rich find. There were also fragments of the bones of the wild ass, antelope, rhinoceros, hyena, cattle and even fragments of shells of the eggs of a huge, extinct type of ostrich which was known to have lived during the time that the heavy loess deposits were building up in northern China.

The first site encountered was one of the richest, but the two enthusiastic Jesuit fathers found other dwelling areas in the Shui-tung K'ou basin, all of them yielding similar evidence of human habitation in the form of stone implements, cooking fires and bone deposits. These discoveries convinced the two Jesuit scientists that the area had been inhabited by people of the Old Stone Age during the period that great wind-blown blanket of loess deposits had been descending on the Yellow River Basin.

This was their pronouncement in spite of the fact that nowhere in the deposits were found remains of human skeletons. Only a single human tooth was discovered, but not among the other culture deposits. Rather, it was picked up on the surface of the ground. After careful study, however, it was decided that it probably was a tooth that had once belonged to a man of the Old Stone Age, and hope grew that other human remains might be located in that area eventually. Indeed, it is probable that since that date the Communists' crops of archeologists have been at work there and may possibly have unearthed further traces of Paleolithic man in the area, though no reports of such finds have reached us yet.

That the whole Shui-tung K'ou basin was an almost ideal place for men of the Old Stone Age to live in is proved by the further discoveries of the two Jesuit scientist-priests. There seems to have been sufficient water and vegetation in this basin to provide extremely favorable conditions for a variety of creatures to flourish, yet the surrounding country constituted a vast desert area. Besides the creatures whose bones were found mixed with the campfire ashes of the men of the Old Stone Age, there was evidence of a number of creatures long since extinct. Among them were a type of ele-

phant, the woolly rhinoceros, a kind of camel, wild boar, big-
horn sheep, buffalo, wolf, hyena and numerous rodents and
birds constituting a fauna that could only exist in a lush,
well-watered area. This being true, it must have been paradise for the humans who seemed to have lived by hunting
only, for there was no evidence of the crude agricultural tools
which would be the normal adjunct to farming.

These people of the Old Stone Age were countless generations and many centuries removed from the cave-dwelling
Sinanthropus of Chou-k'ou Tien. They had probably long
since abandoned caves for the simple reason that, following
game trails which provided them with almost their only
source of food, they had to come out of the hills and live in
the steppes country.

They had to be a bold and courageous people to brave the
open spaces, but they had probably learned to make better
weapons, had developed mass hunting techniques and formed
a tribal community that gave them strength and assurance in
numbers. The dwelling sites explored by Fathers Licent and
de Chardin suggested that in each case a group must have
included a number of families. And their dwellings must
have been but a step removed from the original caves; that
is, dugouts in the ground, roofed over, with probably an entrance in the top that could be closed over against the violent
cold that prevailed and windstorms that swept these steppes
areas in the Pleistocene Age.

That the climate was very cold is suggested by the fact that
among the fossil remains found in the loess deposits about
the time these Old Stone Age men make their appearance are
those of the woolly rhinoceros. Fossil evidence of this prehistoric creature has also been found in Europe and in other
areas, and indicates that they were common inhabitants of

the world about the time the Ice Age was slowly receding. And that there were violent winds, sometimes building up to well over a hundred miles an hour and carrying blinding clouds of yellow dust, is evident from the great blanket of loess soil, or yellow earth, which covers almost all of northern China in varying depths up to three hundred feet.

While the Chinese refer to this yellow earth as Huang-t'u, the scientists call it loess. It was named by the German scholar and explorer, Richthofen, who compared it with similar soil deposits in the Rhine River valley. Dr. Andersson describes it as a grayish-yellow dust that has been carried across the landscape by the wind and deposited where craggy highlands reduced the velocity of the wind so the dust was dropped out and deposited in valleys and sheltered areas, ultimately forming a broad flat plain.

During the arid ages of its formation when there was no rain and therefore no surface run-off, it became a broad level plain with the naked, wind-scoured peaks protruding grimly through this far-flung blanket of yellow earth. How long drought conditions lasted, it is impossible to tell. It was long enough to build up a surface covering of this very fine wind-borne dust to a thickness described by Andersson as being nearly two hundred feet deep in some places in Shensi and Kansu.

Unquestionably the winds were terrifically strong, and the great clouds of yellow dust they picked up in the desert area of Central Asia must have been blinding in their density. Even today there are loess storms that cause the natives a great deal of discomfort, and with the wind velocity so very much greater, as it is known to have been, people of the Old Stone Age must have experienced some very trying periods, to say the least.

How often these heavy winds and loess storms occurred and how long they lasted is hard to determine, of course, but certain evidence indicates that they were intermittent. At times they may have lasted so long that they drove men and beasts to seek whatever shelter it was possible for them to find under such conditions. An interesting opportunity for speculation on the violence of these storms is afforded by the finding of a number of prehistoric ostrich eggs, the shells of some of which were also found by Licent and de Chardin in the Neolithic home sites they discovered in the Shui-tung K'ou basin.

At the time these intermittent windstorms, carrying their burden of yellow dust, swept across the face of northern China, the whole area was probably a vast, undrained, grassy steppe providing grazing areas for large herds of a variety of creatures. In the final analysis, these animals were, of course, responsible for attracting the hunting people of the Old Stone Age to the same area.

Among the denizens of the steppes was a huge, flightless bird, actually a type of ostrich, which built its nest in the grass on the surface of the ground. The eggs of this extinct, prehistoric ostrich were even larger than the eggs of the African ostrich of today. And evidence that they were contemporary with men of the Old Stone Age is furnished by the fragments of eggshells found, as mentioned before, by the two Jesuit explorers in the home sites they discovered in the Shui-tung K'ou basin.

As far back as 1857, a fossilized egg of this huge, long-legged bird was discovered in southern Russia near the town of Cherson by a scientist named Brandt, who pronounced it the egg of an extinct ostrich he called *Struthiolithus chernensis*. An American scientist, Eastman, found one of these fossilized eggs not far from Kalang in northern China in 1898 and readily identified it as the egg of the prehistoric ostrich. Later, at long intervals, others were discovered, and in 1923 Dr. Andersson was able to report in his *Essays on the Cenozoic of Northern China* that altogether nearly eighteen had been unearthed in various places in the provinces of Shantung, Chihli, Shansi, and Honan in northern China.

Dr. Andersson, during his research in China, made a study of these eggs. He found, among other things, that they had been discovered even before the Russian scientist found one at Cherson-chersin. One of the fossils existed in the collection of the Emperor Ch'ien-lung at the art museum in Peking. Fragments of one were also found in the dwelling site of the Painted Pottery People at Yang-shao ts'un, in Honan, when Andersson discovered the Yang Shao culture. These fragments were found in a way that made it quite evident these prehistoric people of the Late Stone Age had unearthed the egg, and since the ostrich responsible for it had been extinct many centuries by that time, they were probably completely baffled by the question of what kind of an egg it was and where it came from.

It was Dr. Andersson who established that the eggs were all found in the loess soil. This was emphasized, the Swedish scientist says, when, after talking with a curio dealer who sold him an egg fossil that had been damaged by a digging pick, he went to the village of Kou-yu Kou and looked up the peasant who had found it. There he was led into a cave that had been dug into the loess to be used as a storeroom beside the peasant's dwelling cave. The man pointed out to the scientist just where and how he had found the egg, and indicated that it had been so buried in the loess soil he had driven his pick into it before he discovered it. He also said that he had seen some other fragments of a fossil egg imbedded in the walls of the recently dug storeroom.

The Swedish scientist began to explore the area indicated by the Chinese farmer and presently dug out of the loess not only fragments of a fossil egg, but several complete eggs. They were all located in a position which left no doubt they had been part of a clutch of ostrich eggs that had once been in a nest on the surface of the ground. When one of the terrific windstorms sweeping across the steppes made it impossible for the brooding bird to stay on her nest, she abandoned it and ran for shelter if any was to be found. Then the wind-blown dust began to settle over the nest and the eggs, burying them so completely that they were never found again by the mother if she indeed survived the storm and was able to search for them.

Those great clouds of yellow dust, that intermittently swept across northern China, enshrouding the land in blinding curtains of choking loess, effectively veiled the fate of the people of the Old Stone Age in Asia. Up to the present there are no definite clues as to whether they tried to stay in their home sites and fight against extinction by the wind-borne peril or whether, like the great ostrich, they abandoned their dwelling places and fled before the yellow storm to more comfortable areas. Since there were no human remains found in the dwelling sites, the latter is assumed to have happened. Possibly they drifted southward toward the tropics, or eastward and northward, ultimately to find the great land bridge that carried them eventually to North America. Some may also have gone to Japan or other Pacific islands.

At any rate, at present they are lost to us for aeons, nor is there much evidence to indicate that northern China was peopled by human beings at all until well after the end of the great dust storms. Then once again traces of man appear on the vast, lush, loess-created steppes over which roamed great herds of all kinds of game.

This is the dawn of the New Stone Age in China and here we find a Neolithic people with the beginnings of a culture that seems suddenly so well established and developed as to suggest that it has come up through many centuries of striving for human progress. Where these people came from and where they learned agriculture and the domestication of animals; where they perfected the polished stone ax, the adz, stone chisels and stone hoes; where they learned the art of making beautifully symmetrical stone arrowheads, spinning whorls of stone, and delicate sewing needles of bone are all unsolved mysteries. But where—above all else—they learned how to make beautiful pottery, quite superior to anything known up to their time, and where they learned the art of painting their pieces with artistic design are questions for which scientists and those who have a layman's interest in prehistoric people are striving to find an answer.

Dr. Andersson was the first to discover evidence of these people of the New Stone Age at Yang-shao Ts'un in Honan Province. He called them the Painted Pottery People and was once of the opinion that they flourished about 3000 B.C. There are others, however, who think the period of their culture might have started very much earlier. Indeed, they are thought to be the people who worked their way up out of the limbo of barbaric ignorance to build the foundations of man's present knowledge, ages before even the remotest period so far traceable in human history.

It was one of the collectors the Swedish geologist employed while he was working for the Chinese Central Government who found the first clues that finally led to the discovery of the culture of the Painted Pottery People. Dr. Andersson, in addition to carrying on his exploration of the mining resources of China, continued to have a deep interest in fossil vertebrates, and every chance he got he or his collectors would search likely districts for more specimens. There were several areas the scientist wanted explored further; in particular, the Hsin-an and Mien-ch'in districts, but it was two years after the first discovery before Dr. Andersson was able to send his collector, then Mr. Liu Chang-sha, into these sections for further exploration. While Liu was instructed to collect fossil remains, Dr. Andersson suggested that he keep his eyes open for any Stone Age objects that might turn up in his search, little dreaming that he was opening the way to discoveries almost as important as those that had to do with Peking man.

Liu was gone about two months, but when he got back to Peking to report to Dr. Andersson, besides a valuable collection of fossils, he displayed a remarkable assortment of stone axes, knives, arrowheads and literally hundreds of other objects that had been fashioned and used by people of the Late Stone Age. Many of them were beautifully shaped and polished and in excellent condition. The Swedish scientist was delighted but a little surprised to learn that Liu had not found these implements himself. Instead he had bought them all from farmers who had turned them up during their plowing and planting over the years.

Dr. Andersson became quite excited over these finds and was desperately eager to visit the district himself because he was sure more important discoveries were to be made there. But it was not until the following year that he was able to go to Honan on other quests; for instance, the eggs of the prehistoric ostrich, which interested him particularly. Happily, he found it possible also to take enough time to look into the story of the finds Mr. Liu had brought home.

One pleasant April day, after a study of the terrain in the vicinity of Mien-ch'ih (about fifty miles due west of Loyang), he started on a walking trip up the road toward the hamlet of Yang-shao Ts'un about six miles distant. This road wound through ravines, arroyos and washed-out areas, the high banks of which were further riven by gullies which revealed the stratigraphy of the district. It was these water-worn banks that Dr. Andersson's experienced eyes searched diligently in the hope of finding the type of deposit he felt sure would produce the kinds of Stone Age implements his collector had brought back to Peking with him.

For a while he was disappointed, but when he had gone something less than a mile, the road led through a very steep-banked ravine, the sides of which showed numerous wash-outs. In one of these he detected ashy soil that was unquestionably a cultural layer which seemed to contain bits of pottery. This looked to the geologist as if it might be of considerable interest, if it were not indeed the actual stratum in which stone implements were to be found. So he climbed the bank and began to dig about with his hands, presently to turn up a fragment of pottery that at first deeply disappointed him and made him temporarily give up the quest on which he had started.

The bit of ceramics was a piece of fine red pottery, beautifully polished, with black painted decorations. In fact, the whole thing was so artistically made that Dr. Andersson could not associate it with Stone Age weapons. He was sure it was a product of pottery makers of a much later generation if not, in fact, of the present. Stone Age people were supposed to be incapable of craftsmanship and artistic efforts equal to that tiny piece of broken ware he held in his hand. With waning enthusiasm he followed this stratum down the road clear to Yang-shao Ts'un, inspecting it wherever it revealed itself. But he wasted little effort on it because he was convinced it had nothing to do with the Neolithic people who made those stone weapons.

So when he reached Yang-shao Ts'un, he established his headquarters there and, forgetting about the Stone Age people with some effort and much disappointment, he continued pursuing his interest in fossilized ostrich eggs that might be buried in the loess, for he was eager to determine the approximate time in which these great flightless birds were extant. Happily, he was able to locate one of these eggs, dig it out of the loess himself, and settle to his satisfaction the age in which the creature flourished. But all the time he worked on the problem of the ostrich that piece of red painted pottery kept naggingly intruding into his thoughts until finally it insisted on being investigated further.

Accordingly, when he had finished with his study of the prehistoric bird, before packing up and leaving Yang-shao Ts'un he decided to devote at least one whole day to making sure in his own mind that the red pottery and the stone implements were not related. It was not difficult for him to pick up axes and other Stone Age objects thereabouts for the boys of the village, knowing he was a collector, brought him a number of fine specimens which he bought for a few coppers each. He was also able to find some himself on the farms south of the village. He could see the heavy streak of ashy deposits in the eroded banks along the road below the village, too, and finally selecting an inviting spot, he began to dig into it with true collector's zeal.

He found more shards of the handsome red pottery, but,

more than that, it was not long before he unearthed an excellent example of a Stone Age tool; a *pen,* or stone adz. Soon other objects began to turn up in such a way that there could be no doubt that the artisans who made these tools were also responsible for the painted pottery found in the stratum along with them. Dr. Andersson realized he had made a tremendously interesting archeological find, but he still felt a little confused by the whole situation. He only wished he had more time and more authority to dig further, for he felt sure that greater revelation awaited him.

As a matter of fact, he had already devoted more time to this personal exploration than he felt he should, so he hastened back to Peking with his mind troubled by a number of questions. But as it happened, he had many of them answered back home in the capital where, in his own library in the offices of the Geological Survey, he ran across the reports of one of his predecessors in the role of geologist for the Chinese Government. He was an American named Raphael Pumpelly who had done a great deal of exploration work in Asia: in Manchuria, China, and Siberia, as well as Russian Turkestan. In this last place he had unearthed some painted pottery of almost exactly the same kind as that found by Dr. Andersson at Yang-shao. The Swedish scientist read also, in other sources, reports of similar polychrome pottery being unearthed in southern Europe; all in Neolithic sites.

This convinced Dr. Andersson he really had made an important discovery in China, and he developed an irresistible desire to get together a crew of diggers and assistants to explore the area just south of Yang-shao Ts'un. He was sure he could find the home site of the people who had come so far in the craft of pottery making and the art of decorating their ware so as to suggest a cultural development of considerable age and importance.

The Painted   5
Pottery People

Up to the time that Dr. Andersson found those shards of painted pottery in the roadside embankments below the village of Yang-shao Ts'un, it was generally believed that the Chinese had known how to work and use bronze from the beginning of their civilization, and that stone implements belonged strictly to the tribes of barbarians lingering in the hinterland. With this idea accepted and quite firmly fixed in his mind the good doctor was both disturbed and confused and forced off balance, so to speak, when confronted by the fact that the people of the ancient Yang-shao Ts'un area unquestionably used polished stone tools at a time when they also showed complete mastery of the art of pottery making.

As far as he was concerned, there was no evidence at all that they had any knowledge of copper or any other metal. And yet painted pottery of a very similar character to that he had found was attributed to people of the early Metal Age by Pumpelly and other explorers when they unearthed shards of it in Turkestan and southern Europe. Could it be that the

Yang-shao people had learned and developed the craft of pottery making long before Neolithic people in other areas of the world? In fact, was it not possible that the art had been developed by the Chinese in the very distant past and had radiated slowly in many directions? This was a very exciting thought. Possibly the Painted Pottery People furnished the evidence needed to establish as authentic the contention that China was indeed the source of the oldest civilization in the world. Or was it possible that exactly the reverse was true? It could very well be that the art of making pottery was brought into China by the migration of people from southern Europe or those who may have come from Turkestan.

Others who talked to the Swedish scientist were no less eager to search for the home site of the Yang-shao people, but in spite of their interest it was several months before Dr. Andersson could get official permission and the complete co-operation of the Minister of Agriculture, the Geological Survey and the local authorities in the province of Honan to carry on exploration work there. Finally, however, all arrangements were made and crews assembled, and Dr. Andersson, accompanied by Dr. Zdansky, Dr. Davidson Black, Miss Elsa Rosenius, the Swedish scientist whom Andersson later married, and five Chinese scientific confreres, Messrs. Chang, Chen, Liu, Yao and Pai, traveled to Mien-ch'ih Hsien, the district in which Yang-shao is located, and proceeded with their excavations.

It became apparent to everyone at the outset that the area of prehistoric cultural deposits located south of the small present-day village of Yang-shao was very large and very rich in material as archeological sites go in China and elsewhere. It covered roughly a section 2,000 feet north and south and about the same distance east to west and formed something of an island between deep ravines eroded in the loess plateau. The cultural deposits themselves were from four to twenty feet deep and contained an amazing quantity of artifacts including potsherds, burial urns and a marvelous collection of polished stone implements. Among the latter were greenstone axes, stone adzes, stone knives, baked clay bracelets, arrowheads and a host of other Neolithic tools, not the least of which were spinning whorls, indicating that these people had also mastered the art of weaving. But nowhere was there evidence of any knowledge of the use of metals.

Arrowheads were found made of stone, bone and shell, and all were well formed, indicating a high degree of craftsmanship. The spinning whorls were made of both stone and fire-burnt clay. But of course the biggest collection of artifacts was pottery, both the painted variety and cups, dishes and bowls made of coarser brown-gray or entirely grayish ceramics. Interestingly enough, here also appeared stages of the development of the traditionally Chinese urns with pointed bottoms and the tripod vessels, both of the *li* and the *ting* type. Unearthed also were fragments of an ingenious double vessel used for steaming, called a *hsien,* which took on the qualities of a sacred vessel and was used for burials at a much later date. These tripod forms have survived the ages and are in common use today in many rural sections of China.

It was, however, the remarkably fine quality of the painted pottery Dr. Andersson's expedition brought to light that held the interest of Sinologists both in China and in the west. The fact that comparable ware both from the standpoint of quality and decoration had been found in other areas, particularly in Europe, thousands of miles from the great central plains of China posed some interesting problems. This pottery was of excellent workmanship; very thin, beautifully finished and with a very high polish. Dr. Andersson thought the objects had been finished with a coating of finely ground clay mixed with pigment known as slip, which provided a colorful and smooth working surface on which to paint the decorations. Black and red were the predominating colors, with which white was combined on a few objects.

So extensive were these cultural remains that it was felt that the Yang-shao village must have been a very large Neolithic community.* Occasional skeletons were found during the excavation, and finally a cemetery area was located from which were exhumed seventeen nearly complete skeletons and other scattered remains. On the whole, however, this grave exploration part of the investigation was quite disappointing.

The excavators did unearth one feature that caused considerable interest and speculation. They found a number of pits or pockets having a peculiar inverted wedge shape with the wide area at the bottom. These pits were not graves because in no instance did they find evidence of human remains interred in them. Mostly the pits were filled with ashes, fragments of broken pottery and other artifacts. This suggested that they were refuse pits. But that did not seem a logical reason for their existence. Dr. Davidson Black recalled that while exploring an Indian village site in Madisonville, Ohio, similar pits of exactly the same shape were found which were called cache pits and which it was believed were used as a kind of cold cellar for storing grain and other provisions to be carried over for a long period of time.

It was finally agreed that these Yang-shao pits were also

---

* It has recently been suggested (1960) that the site was a village of intermittent habitation. People lived there until the fields were exhausted, moved away and came back again when the soil was fertile once more.

storage pits of much the same order, because evidence of the storage of seeds was found in some of them. When the pits were empty, they became trash pits until they had to be cleaned out for storage purposes again after another harvest. This also contributed to the realization that the Painted Pottery People had a knowledge of agriculture. Indeed, a later discovery that they used fronds of the rice plant for decorative purposes on some ceramics verified this.

It has also been suggested that the pits may have been dwelling pits, but these seem to have been exceedingly crude houses for people who had advanced as far culturally as they had. It is conceivable, however, that the pits may have been cellars under dugout dwellings.

Another interesting discovery was the shafts of several fairly deep wells completely dry and filled with ashy earth. There were imprints of log beams that had been laid across the top doubtless used to support hoisting gear by means of which to raise the water from the well. The fact that the wells were located on the loess plateau and that the present water table was found to be more than one hundred feet below the deepest of the wells indicated to Dr. Andersson that a great geological change had taken place over the thousands of years since the Painted Pottery People had dug them and used them as a village water supply.

Dr. Andersson's discovery of the Yang-shao culture created a great deal of interest among scientists, but more than that, it aroused in him a much deeper interest in archeology than he had ever had before. He began to consider the possibility of making his geological investigations secondary to his search for artifacts that might help him trace the history of the Painted Pottery People he had discovered. While he did not actually abandon his work as a geologist, he very definitely kept the search for more evidence of the Yang-shao culture constantly in mind, and never missed an opportunity to investigate every new clue that came to his attention.

As a result of this, he almost immediately encountered an enigma that caused him and later his associate, Dr. Davidson Black, considerable speculative thought, to say the least. The Swedish scientist was directed by the Ministry of Agriculture to look into coal reserves and other mineral resources in a section of southern Manchuria not far from Sha-kuo T'un, the terminus of a branch of the Peking-Mukden Railroad. There, having some free time to spare for archeology, Dr. Andersson directed two collectors, Yao and Pai, and a young interpreter named James Wong to investigate a series of caves in the limestone hills which the natives had pointed out to the geologist.

Almost immediately after they began to dig into the cave deposits they brought to light a number of objects which made it evident the cave contained a tremendous amount of material of prehistoric value, and Dr. Andersson took personal charge of the exploration. Several weeks were devoted to the task of completely emptying the cave of its deep deposits of fine gray sand in which was found some very baffling evidence of human occupancy. Among them was a strangely scrambled collection of human bones. These required the efforts of a trained anatomist to investigate intelligently, and Dr. Andersson telegraphed to Dr. Davidson Black. He hastened from his post at the Peking Union Medical College and arrived in time to be of great assistance as the cave was emptied of the last of its deposits.

Of the utmost importance to Dr. Andersson, though disappointing in numbers, were the pieces of painted pottery that were found in the lower and bottom deposits. They were from urns and other fairly large vessels. There were a number of polished stone implements, arrowheads, and four stone axes, all so small as to suggest that they were made in miniature. There were also fragments of a strange collection of rings, some of bracelet size and many smaller. There were marble beads and marble buttons and one strange little figurine of whitish-yellow marble that suggested a cat. This had a hole in it that would permit it to be worn on a string, possibly along with the beads.

But the most baffling find of all was the tremendous mass of human bones with no suggestion of orderly arrangement. Indeed, the remains of more than forty human beings, including men, women and children, were unearthed there and, gruesomely enough, the bones were shattered in such a way as to suggest to Dr. Black that they might have been crushed while they were still fresh, possibly for the purpose of extricating the marrow from them. This and other factors immediately raised the question of cannibalism and the suspicion that the cave may have been a den of barbaric savages. It was also suggested that it may have been used for burial purposes, but the general disorder of the bones and the lack of other funeral arrangements seemed to make this interpretation improbable.

With further thought it seemed to the explorers, however, that the cave might well have been a sanctuary or temple of a cult of Stone Age people who conducted gruesome ritual meetings there, an important part of which included human sacrifice. The figurine, the heads, and the series of rings, many of them made very delicately of fragile mussel shell, all may have played a part in any cult ceremonies. But, of course, all of this was speculative reasoning at best and there was no conclusive evidence of the meanings of the finds in the cave at

Sha-kuo T'un beyond the fact that the human beings who left them were contemporaries of the Painted Pottery People.

Probably because he was a westerner himself, Dr. Andersson wanted to believe that the migration of people eastward from Europe had been responsible for bringing the art of pottery making to China. He supported his belief, of course, by relying on the close resemblance of the painted ware of the Yang-shao culture with the ceramics that had been found nearly two decades earlier by Pumpelly in Russian Turkestan, and these in turn resembled strongly the painted ceramics from eastern Europe.

The more the Swedish scientist thought of this, the stronger grew his feeling that by tracing the evidence of the migration eastward across China he might prove his contention. He knew the country well enough to believe he could work out a logical path of migration, and so convinced did he become that he knew almost the very mountain pass by which the western immigrants would enter China that he finally decided on leading an expedition to explore sections of what he believed to be the probable migration route. He knew desert areas would be avoided and that the migrants would keep to the lush, flat steppe area, and probably follow along the foot of the Nan Shan Mountains, crossing the Yellow River near Lanchow, moving diagonally in a southeast direction along the T'ao River and across the present provinces of Kansu and Shensi and into Honan, where he discovered the Painted Pottery People at Yang-shao.

One of the things that probably inspired Dr. Andersson to undertake this mission was the fact that he had some knowledge of at least one Neolithic dwelling site along the route he had in mind. It had been discovered by his collectors, Chang and Dr. Zdansky, when they made an expedition into eastern Kansu the previous year, and he was convinced that there were more to be found as they moved northwestward along the route he had in mind.

There were other dwelling sites and Dr. Andersson found them, but unhappily, most of them were disappointing in the quantity of Yang-shao artifacts that were unearthed. Shards of painted pottery were found, to be sure, but never in sufficient quantity to convince Dr. Andersson beyond a doubt that he had found the route by which this culture had come to China, if indeed it truly had been introduced by people from eastern Europe.

He and his group of explorers pushed on determinedly in the direction the scientist was convinced the flow of migration had followed, but with meager and unsatisfactory results. Finally Dr. Andersson promised rewards up to one hundred dollars to the first member of the expedition to turn up a significant find that would lead to the location of a really productive Neolithic dwelling site.

It fell to his cook, one Chuang, to spot a fragment of painted pottery protruding from an ashy cultural layer in the roadside embankment near Shih-li P'u. After securing permission from the authorities, the expedition spent a week exploring this area in a very systematic way. They found the dwelling site they were convinced was located there and exhumed a fine collection of Neolithic implements of stone and bone. They also found many fragments of the Yang-shao pottery, as well as a much coarser type of pottery which Dr. Andersson felt was of a more recent date.

From there they tried to follow the trail of Painted Pottery culture northwestward right to the fringes of Tibetan territory into the basin of the great salt lake known as Koko Nor. But the exploration in this area was not as profitable as the

Swedish scientist had hoped, although they did find some evidence of early Yang-shao people in flint weapons which were quite numerous. As a matter of fact, ultimately such a great quantity of shaped and unshaped flints were found that the question arose whether these Stone Age people have been attracted to this area to replenish their supplies of flint (a type of material rare in China) instead of following a migration route.

All this was quite baffling and Dr. Andersson concluded after two weeks' effort in the vicinity of the great salt lake that his migration theory was far from proved. In fact, he acknowledged ruefully that all he had unearthed was a number of confusing problems that needed considerably more study.

Disappointed in a measure, the expedition followed a somewhat different route eastward over the steppe country, still searching hopefully for dwelling sites that would prove measurably near as rich as the Yang-shao site in Honan. But if this portion of the journey did not produce the archeological treasure desired, it certainly provided excitement and adventure. The Tibetan residents of a village on Chinese soil near which they camped while they explored the area resented their intrusion and began to make trouble. At one point it became a question whether a serious shooting affray might not result.

But Dr. Andersson with a firm show of authority, backed up by his passport and official papers from the Central Government, invaded the town with his soldier guards and members of his expedition and bearded the headman in his home. There the scientist demanded proper respect be accorded him and his men and restitution made for a stolen horse and an injured mule. The situation was very tense for a while, but finally the headman complied with the conditions and as-

When Dr. S. Howard Hanford visited Anyang, he found that, even during a time of war, treasure hunting was very active. Here are natives searching for Shang bronzes in their own dooryard. One is operating an auger to locate pounded earth indicating the presence of a tomb. (Photo by Dr. S. H. Hanford)

Dr. Hanford said that when a valuable bronze was found the farmer owning the land, the diggers, dealers and all parties concerned held a conference to determine price and the best methods of protecting it from bandits and rapacious Japanese soldiers. (Photo by Dr. S. H. Hanford)

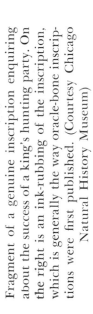

Fragment of a genuine inscription enquiring about the success of a king's hunting party. On the right is an ink-rubbing of the inscription, which is generally the way oracle-bone inscriptions were first published. (Courtesy Chicago Natural History Museum)

Two forgeries. Note the sharp, deep lines and smooth curves of characters inscribed on left-hand fragment; no mineral deposits, obvious forgery. Both bones are genuinely old but the carving on both was added recently. (Courtesy Chicago Natural History Museum)

Preliminary exploration of the fissure which later became known as the cave of Peking Man. (Photo by O. Zdansky)

BONE-DEPOSIT

Looking WNW at the Chou-k'ou Tien site from across the valley. White patches on mountains are quarry scars. (Photo by O. Zdansky)

The great oracle-bone pit has been carefully surrounded by a wooden wall and its contents are being painstakingly removed under the broiling midsummer sun.

Cutting away the earth below a priceless bronze vessel while measuring its exact location and attitude. This was the entire contents of burial no. 188. See Map 3.

Painted Pottery bowl from Pan-p'o Ts'un near Sian, discovered and restored by Communist "archeological workers," which is said to supply a rather important link between the Painted Pottery People and the people of the Shang State.

Pounded earth foundations and pillar foundations at the Shang City site.

Shang bronzes are regarded as priceless but when a collector is willing to part with one, which happens on rare occasions, the price asked may range anywhere from two thousand to ten thousand dollars. (Courtesy of the Smithsonian Institution, Freer Gallery of Art, Washington, D.C.)

sured the explorer that they would not be interfered with again.

As a result they spent a week investigating a site that had been pointed out by an old man who the villagers insisted was mad. It proved to be a true Yang-shao site and produced interesting implement and pottery finds. But the most important discovery was the burned floors of what had undoubtedly been Neolithic kilns in which the painted pottery had been baked. Portions of the clay walls of the ovens were still intact and the bottoms were of burnt clay over a bed of rubble. This was an unusual and to Dr. Andersson a very satisfactory find, for the remains of very few kilns had been located up to that time.

The polished stone implements taken out of this site, which was known as the Lo-han T'ang dwelling site, included some rare specimens, not the least of which was a peculiar stone knife shaped like extended bird's wings. Dr. Andersson felt that this site, almost as far west as Koko Nor but near the Yellow River, was one of the oldest of the Neolithic sites that had yet been discovered.

Another important find was made at a village called Chu-chia after Dr. Andersson and his group had returned to their old headquarters in Hsi-ning, one hundred miles west of Lanchow on the old silk route. The Swedish scientist returned there because he remembered seeing along the roadside in a cut bank some small fragments which suggested that more important finds might be turned up if considerable digging were done. He had kept this location in the back of his mind as worth looking into on his return journey, and as soon as they had set up their quarters in Hsi-ning the leader sent out two of his men to look into the deposit exposed in the cut bank. It was not difficult to locate the prehistoric dwelling site, for it covered a fairly large area, extending almost into the heart of the modern village, which made digging fairly difficult.

The residents were not pleased to have foreign devils move in and begin digging in their dooryards. All arrangements, however, were finally completed diplomatically and work was started very soon, for everyone was eager to look for archeological treasures. They were not long in turning up, either, for soon several burial urns were found by the excavators.

But it was only after considerable search that the heart of the graveyard area was located. It presented an enigma, however, the answer to which was not immediately apparent. All the graves were very deep, and added to that, they seemed to have been disturbed by something. It was found that matching portions of broken urns were widely separated from each other and at different levels. The work of grave robbers and the digging of peasants did not seem to account for this, and there appeared to be no answer until it was discovered that there had been a heavy earthquake in that section of the province several years before and lighter temblors had been felt from time to time since. It became evident then that this shifting of the earth had moved some of the funerary furniture from its original location and disturbed many of the graves.

The whole area proved to be very rich in objects of the Yang-shao culture, however. Forty-three skeletons were discovered, with a plethora of burial furniture of all types ranging from urns to beads, knives and a host of other objects. Bone armor, buried with its warrior owner, was considered to be among the most important discoveries made there.

Several weeks were spent in working over this site, for some of the finds were so fragile and delicate that nothing heavier than a camel's-hair brush could be used to remove the earth. The soil had to be worked away very gently until the skeletons and the accompanying material lay on top of a tiny plateau of earth. Then the earth was impregnated with a substance that made it very hard, and the whole unit was removed just as a block of stone would be taken out of a quarry.

In all, over the period of years Dr. Andersson was working in China he explored more than forty Yang-shao dwelling sites. The largest and most productive was the first he discovered in Honan province, the type site from which the culture takes its name. The second largest and richest was the Chi-chia Chai burial site mentioned above. But never in any of his explorations was he able to bridge the vast gap of aeons between the men of the Old Stone Age who lived on the edge of the Ordos Desert and men of the New Stone Age as represented by the Yang-shao Painted Pottery People. So he never did prove to his satisfaction the theory that this art of painted pottery making had come into China from the west. Indeed, as time went on, he began to change his opinion.

He seemed to feel that this culture may have originated in the Honan-Shansi area and the migration might possibly have been westward toward Europe. Other noted archeologists advanced much the same opinion.

Since the Communists with their vaunted "25,000 archeologists" (which seems to be an incredible number even as a boast) have taken over, they insist that they have uncovered literally hundreds of sites of Painted Pottery People (Yang-shao) and a related Neolithic culture known as Chi-chia culture in the Kansu area according to reports in the two principal publications of the Ministry of Science, *K'ao-ku T'ung-hsün* and the *K'ao-ku Hsüeh-pao*.

Along the dusty roads which fan out from almost every

large city with a past in north China may be discovered a place named Shih-li P'u (literally Ten-mile Store). Twice that distance down the road away from the city walls is probably a Twenty-mile Store as well. These settlements doubtless arose because they were a convenient journey from the city. Sian, the ancient capital of the Chou people, due west of where the Yellow River turns abruptly eastward, has its Shih-li P'u on the road (wide and paved now) which runs along the Wei River. Near there on the slopes which eventually rise to form the frowning tops of the sacred mountain, Hua-shan, one of the most fascinating finds of the last decade, was made. An entire Neolithic village of the Painted Pottery People was uncovered by the "archeological workers" in blue coveralls near what was the present-day hamlet of Pan-p'o Ts'un.

Dr. T'ang Lan in his report on this discovery said that they had uncovered positive evidence of advanced development in the stone, pottery and bone industries. The latter, he said, seemed to be unexpectedly well developed and included, among other interesting things, fishhooks on which barbs were used. It was also evident that they had learned how to store grain successfully. Outstanding in the discoveries were two painted bowls that were restored to excellent condition and found to have decorations which were believed to supply a rather important link between the Painted Pottery People and the people of the Shang State, whose capital was revealed through the oracle bones found at Anyang. The significance of this has not yet been fully determined.

It is interesting to learn that all of the area that has so far been uncovered of the village at Pan-p'o Ts'un has been roofed over and elevated wooden walkways have been built across the excavated site so that it has become a museum in itself. According to the best information available, more of this well-defined and well-preserved village was to have been excavated in 1959.

Further to the west, past the headwaters of the Wei River and all along the T'ao and Ta-hsia rivers—tributaries to the Yellow River which join it near the capital city of Kansu, Lanchow—while extensive motor road and railroad building was going on, the Chinese archeologists uncovered scores of Neolithic sites of these same Painted Pottery People, and the Communists insist that an enormous amount of information has now been collected about the area which Dr. Andersson first explored almost forty years ago. Little of this has reached the United States.

Two Neolithic Cultures   6

U<small>ntil</small> Dr. Andersson began the pioneering work which resulted in discovery of the Yang-shao Painted Pottery People in 1921, it had been generally assumed that there had never been a stage in prehistoric China which corresponded to the Neolithic. Even such an authority as Berthold Laufer of the Field Museum in Chicago felt that a stone age for China was inadmissible. As mentioned before, it was an accepted belief that their culture had its beginning in the early Metal Age, but when Dr. Andersson made his discovery of the Painted Pottery culture in western China and almost at the same time or very shortly thereafter the so-called Black Pottery culture was discovered in northeastern China, it gradually became quite clear that not only one but two different Neolithic societies had flourished during the period between 3000 and 1000 B.C. The problem then became less a question of whether the art of Painted Pottery had spread toward Europe from China or whether the reverse was true. Instead, it became a fascinating study of which of these two Neolithic cultures was the older.

Today it seems relatively certain that the Black Pottery culture of the east coast was earlier and stayed longer than did the Painted Pottery makers, even though in some sites, in particular at Hou Kang near Hsian-t'un, close to which the Shang City site is located (of which more will be written later), the red pottery of the Yang-shao type was found in a layer below the Black Pottery. There it would seem the Yang-shao people lived before the Black Pottery makers moved in. But in any case it is abundantly clear that both cultures had thrived and declined before that area became the place where the history of China begins—about 1300 B.C.

It was a Chinese archeologist, Wu Chin-ting, who discovered Ch'eng-tzu-yai, the Black Pottery culture site at Lung-shan Chen (see Map 1) in the province of Shantung. He thereby brought to light still another Neolithic culture in China, and by so much dispelled some of the dense fog that obscures the centuries between the prehistoric and the historic era that now begins with the Shang City-State at Anyang.

It was known for some time that there was a prehistoric dwelling site near Lung-shan Chen; in fact, several of them, namely, Ch'eng-tzu-yai, P'ing-ling, and Chu-li Ch'eng. Wu intended one day to look into all of them, for some interesting artifacts had been picked up in that vicinity. In fact, he made two quick trips there and on the second one he made a notable discovery at Ch'eng-tzu-yai, about which he wrote: ". . . at ten in the morning I arrived at the village of (Dragon Hill County) Lung-shan Chen. Accompanied by Mr. Chang, I went to a deep gully north of the village and set about investigating it. I had just reached a high vantage point on the south face of the gully when I looked eastward from the village, and in the distance I saw a raised area which had the appearance of a low city wall. I consulted with Mr. Chang as to whether this was the raised area which we had passed on our way to P'ing-ling previously, the place whose stratum of gray earth I had suspected."

Evidently Chang agreed that it was the place Wu had mentioned previously, and felt it was worthy of investigation, according to Dr. Kenneth Starr, of the Chicago Natural History Museum, the translator of a great deal of material about Ch'eng-tzu-yai, published by the Yale University Press, for Wu continued:

". . . We then dropped our work at the gully north of the village and turning toward the southeast, moved along quickly. We saw evidences of fire and the deposition of red (or burned) earth was quite thick. The places where there had been fires seemed to have a definite appearance. The gray-earth cultural stratum on the cliff was quite clear and in the stratum were such things as sherds and pieces of stone, shell and bone. These objects were like the ones that we usually saw. Within a short time we had dug out two bone awls. The crudeness of their manufacture was quite enough to indicate their antiquity. I could not help being overjoyed. What I had suspected on former occasions was actually proved true today! If the site held this type of potsherd and bone implement, then it would surely contain such things as stone axes and stone knives, and we could certainly expect future discoveries.

"We carefully examined the containing layer, but there were no fragments of brick or tile, there was nothing of metal, there were no fragments of porcelain, and no traces of cinders. The characteristics of this site were very different from those at P'ing-ling (a nearby site that revealed only evidence of more recent occupancy), and it is needless to say that this was older. Upon climbing the cliff and inspecting the surface, we found that the remains were very disorderly. Along with the numerous potsherds from such types as the *tou* (stem dishes) and *li* (tripod) there were also quite a few recent objects and human leavings. Accumulations of cinders were evident in several places, but I suspected that either later peoples had lived there or that they were materials which later peoples had brought from elsewhere.

"We then went to the top of the cliff to dig out some potsherds as samples and as souvenirs of the trip. After this I began definitely to realize the great significance of the cultural stratum at this site."

Sometime later Wu, and presumably Mr. Chang, visited the site again and began exploring the gully once more. He wrote:

"Following the north bank of the gully by the main road . . . we proceeded northward, and at the northeast corner of the site, I saw that the layer of burned red earth was very thick. In it were mixed gray and black potsherds. I then began digging . . . cutting out a sloping hole. At the depth of 17.5 centimeters there appeared a black stone object. I carefully cleared away the red earth surrounding it and removed it. It was a stone ax, complete and not the least bit damaged. All that I had hypothesized earlier, that is to say, my opinion that this site would produce stone implements, thereupon received confirmation."

Wu's revelation of the unusual type of pottery he had discovered at Lung-shan Chen, in Shantung, along with the fact that he had also found Stone Age implements which definitely established the antiquity of the site, created quite a sensation in Chinese archeological circles. All this, of course, came to the attention of the Institute of History and Philology of Academia Sinica and it was not long before further exploration was being urged.

This site was entirely the discovery of Chinese archeologists. No westerners had been concerned in it at all and the suggestion was made that the exploration of the site become exclusively a Chinese project also. Indeed, it was urged that the Academia Sinica and the Shantung Provincial Government join their efforts to form an organization to study this and other sites in the province without foreign assistance. The result was that the Society for the Study of Shantung Antiquities was established and plans were quickly made for excavating at Ch'eng-tzu-yai.

It will be remembered that while Dr. Andersson, with some support from others, felt for a time at least that the Neolithic Painted Pottery culture of Yang-shao had originated in the west and had migrated to China to form the foundation of Chinese culture, there were those, particularly among the Chinese archeologists, who did not wholly agree with him. They did not feel that he had proved his case. They pointed to the fact that Painted Pottery, while found in many western sites, was never discovered in the northeastern part of China. So, when it was known that a distinctive type of pottery which was called Black Pottery was found to predominate in the potsherds that Wu had unearthed at Ch'eng-tzu-yai, they had a feeling that a long missing link in the history of Chinese culture was about to be established.

Dr. Li Chi, a well-known scholar and archeologist, was appointed to the Society for the Study of Shantung Antiquities as a representative of the Academia Sinica. He acted as chief of operations during the first excavation and in an interview with reporters said:

"Looking at the regional distribution of the Neolithic sites which have been discovered, we are still not able to provide complete verification for the 'theory of coming from the west' because the areas which this type of painted pottery occupies are only in the western and northern parts of China. In the great plain in the northeastern part of China such as the southeastern part of the Hoepi Province, the eastern part of the Honan Province and extending into a part of Shantung, there still have been no discoveries of this kind of painted pottery. The result of all this newly accomplished research naturally leads one to think about the following problems:

"Does the great interior plain in northeastern China also have a Neolithic? If the answer is yes, does it also have painted pottery? Ch'eng-tzu-yai occupies a central position in the great northeastern plain and it has produced not only stone implements, but also significant pottery which is of a completely different type from that of the Neolithic sites of the western and northern regions. This type of pottery is a monochrome; its color is black, and it has a gloss like that of lacquer. Its shape bears great resemblance to later bronze implements. This type of Neolithic remains is as yet the first discovery of its kind in interior China, and its relationship with the bronze culture of the Shang and Chou is very close. Its importance is one that those who study this problem recognize immediately."

As soon as Li Chi received full authorization to proceed with the planned excavation at Ch'eng-tzu-yai he organized his staff and established his field headquarters at Lung-shan Chen. Of course, he included among his six staff members the discoverer of the site, Wu Chin-ting. He also included the well-known scholar, Tung Tso-pin, and other members of the Academia Sinica, including Kuo Pao-chün, Li Kuang-yu, and Wang Hsiang.

Workmen were recruited at the scene of the operation, beginning with a crew numbering eighteen at first, which was doubled later when all surveying and other preliminary work was completed. A very important part of this preliminary work was securing permission from the farmers who owned the land in the site area, and persuading them to accept the land-rental program that had been agreed upon by the Society as being equitable. The peasants were always suspicious of strangers who wanted to disturb the earth by digging. They insisted that very bad luck for the whole area always followed such activities.

The first step was to request the District Office to get in touch with the farmers. At the same time the village elders and headmen were assembled at field headquarters and the plan of exploration and reasons for the operation were explained to them, along with a land-rental agreement that would reimburse farmers for any crops that might be disturbed and would provide for all excavations to be refilled.

Because of a late start in November, the work of digging a series of trenches had to be carried out with as much dispatch as possible. It was realized that at best there remained only about a month of good weather before it would become too cold to work in the earth. That turned out to be the true situation, for exactly one month from the day the work started it had to be abandoned because of the winter conditions that were fast developing.

But it was a very productive month. Archeological treasures were numerous indeed, and many really significant finds were made among the 23,878 specimens collected. More than 20,000 of these were, of course, pottery objects ranging from

complete vessels to sherds large enough to have some significance to the collectors who were kept busy cleaning, numbering, cataloguing and otherwise recording them and the details
relating to their discovery. Altogether it was a quite satisfactory operation. The bone, horn, and stone implements unearthed numbered more than 1,800 pieces, and there were
more than 800 shell objects of all types, including tools such
as saws, knives, shovels and, of course, arrowheads.

One of the first facts established by the diggers was the
existence of the remains of what had once been an ancient
city wall, just as Wu Chin-ting had suspected when he saw
the mounds of earth on the upper one of the three terraces
that rose above the old river bed in the valley. Pounded earth
indicating what remained of a long-neglected city wall was
found in the very first area explored. Its condition suggested
that the old wall had been allowed to erode and crumble,
probably while the city site was still partially inhabited. Sub-
sequent investigation revealed that the wall enclosed an area
about 1,500 feet long by 1,200 feet wide. It had been about
thirty feet thick at the base and a few feet less than that across
the top.

It was also established that while the wall had been built
by people of the Black Pottery culture, it had been constructed in two different periods, possibly by two different
generations of dwellers in that particular city site. However,
the Black Pottery People had been living there for some time
before they started to build the wall at all, for black pottery sherds were found under the foundations of the wall in
some places. In other places black pottery sherds were found
in the wall itself, indicating that they had been scooped up
by the builders and pounded into the earth when the wall was
being constructed.

It was also estimated that the wall had survived the erosion of wind and weather and the digging of the dwellers it protected for more than ten centuries before it finally crumbled to the state in which it was found by the archeologists. During this millennium it had been the bulwark of defense for two different groups of people, for it was established that there was a later group inhabiting the site who were known as the Gray Pottery People. Evidence of their presence was found in gray pottery sherds that were revealed in the upper cultural stratum, particularly in the vicinity of the wall.

These latecomers to the site were a much smaller group than the Black Pottery People who had built the city originally and a long time later abandoned it. They appeared to be less progressive than their predecessors, too, for they seemed to accept what was left of the city as a dwelling place, and though the wall had crumbled and eroded a great deal, it was still high enough to give them protection. Evidently they did not have many enemies, for there were no accumulations of arrowheads or weapons at the foot of the wall, indicating that battles had been fought there. In fact, by a similar inference the Black Pottery People had not had many aggressive enemies either, for it was they who first allowed the wall to deteriorate. They even piled their rubbish against it in many different places, and later the people who made the gray pottery had so little interest in the wall that they dug into it to get pottery clay and made tombs in it to bury their dead. They also built numerous kilns in the vicinity in which they baked their gray pottery.

Wu had mentioned in his report of his first visit to the Ch'eng-tzu-yai site that he had noticed in the sides of the gully and other places the presence of red earth, obviously fire burned to a very great degree. Similar areas were found in the vicinity of the old city wall when it was exposed by digging. These burned places indicated that the fires had been much bigger and hotter than anything needed for cooking purposes, and Wu and the rest began to suspect that his first impression of this hard red earth was correct. He had a feeling all along that they were the fire beds of kilns or ovens in which the prehistoric people had baked their pottery.

As the wall was explored it became more and more evident that there had, indeed, been kilns near the wall and even on top of the wall. Some of those exposed revealed the remains of circular fire walls that had been burned hard, so hard, in fact, that they appeared to be a purplish black in color inside the kiln, gradually changing to a gray-green, then a rusty red as the distance increased from the center of greatest heat.

By careful excavation the archeologists were able to get a complete plan of the kilns. They were composed of two compartments; the upper compartment, circular in shape and about four feet in diameter, was the oven portion in which the pottery was baked. This was equipped with four heat vents in its floor and was surrounded by a hard, thoroughly baked gray-green wall that had been lined with smeared clay mixed with cut-up straw.

Under the oven was a fire pit with a capacity as great as, or greater than, that of the oven itself. It was connected with the oven by way of the oval heat vents and surrounded by red burned earth. Evidences of charcoal were to be found in these pits, along with other debris that included sherds, rocks, and in one kiln the skull of a horse which had probably been tossed into it when a portion of one side of the oven had been smashed in.

By the sherds that were mixed with the rubbish found in the different cavities of the kilns the archeologists decided that these ovens had very probably been built and used by the Gray Pottery People who had built their community on a portion of the site of the area that had originally been occupied many centuries before by the Black Pottery People. They were definitely in the upper, or more recent, cultural level.

By far the most numerous artifacts gleaned from the excavation at Ch'eng-tzu-yai were the thousands of potsherds of various sizes. Suggesting as they did the independent development in northeastern China of a culture unlike anything that is known to have existed anywhere else in the world at that period, which is estimated to be around 2000 B.C., they reveal a civilization well advanced for that era. A study of these potsherds indicates that the prehistoric people who inhabited the dwelling site at Ch'eng-tzu-yai possessed great skill and experience in the art of pottery making. Their techniques were well developed, they knew the use of the pottery wheel and were artistic both in designing and shaping their ware, and measurably clever and ingenious in the way they decorated some of the pieces.

In all there were about thirty-five different types of vessels indicated by the sherds of various sizes. These included covered bowls and pots with different kinds of handle projections and feet formations. Here also appears the characteristically Chinese *li* tripod. They had both hollow and solid-legged tripods, and vessels with a variety of different rims, and small, medium, and large-mouthed jars, pitchers and numerous other types, including seven different *tou,* or compote-shaped stem dishes.

Most of the pottery was of the black variety, the most conspicuously beautiful being a very glossy, thin black ware that had a lovely luster and was black all the way through. But of course it varied a great deal. Some were black on the surface and red inside; some were gray; some yellow and some salmon red, all depending, of course, on the material of which each was made and the intensity of the heat it was subjected to in firing.

Four methods of manufacture were reflected, too, for some indicated by finger imprints that they had been shaped entirely by hand and carefully molded with great art and dexterity. Efforts had been made to rub out carefully any evidence of fingerprints, but to the experienced collector's eye there were many telltale marks of hand shaping. Others were made by the impress method, a process still employed, in which a paddle covered with grass or cord is used as a pressing agent against the outside of the vessel, while inside the hand or a rock offers a point of resistance. The grass or cord impression on the surface presents a certain decorative quality that is not unpleasant to look at.

The third method, of course, is the use of the pottery wheel. There is no accurate record of when this was first developed in China. Its use by the Black Pottery People is one of the earliest evidences of its existence, but the skill with which they employed it suggests a very long period of experience. So any reasonably accurate guess as to when it was invented must await archeological discoveries that will raise the curtain, obscuring human history still higher.

Besides the sherds and the few complete pottery vessels that were unearthed by Dr. Li Chi and his staff, a significant number of stone, bone, horn and shell tools were brought to light. They included all the usual articles of Neolithic culture, among them arrowheads of stone, bone and shell, stone axes, adzes, chisels, hammers, grindstones, rubbing stones, shovels, spearheads and ornaments. There were bone awls, bodkins, chisels, hairpins, needles, shuttles and horn awls and chisels.

The shell artifacts included saws, knives, rings and shovels. There were also some bronze artifacts, a few arrowheads and a single knife, all of which suggests that the Black Pottery People were beginning to enter the bronze age. It is important to mention that an inscribed sherd was also found and that many of the fragments of pottery vessels were marked with characters suggesting the potter may have had a method of numbering his wares. There was one piece found that had inscribed on it what appeared to be a line of characters which amounted to writing. Translated, they revealed that the owner was pleased with his prowess as a fisherman, for he saw fit to write down the fact that he had caught six fish and one small turtle; probably he had put them in the large pottery jar from which the sherd had broken. This indicated quite clearly that the Black Pottery People could express themselves in a fairly well-developed form of writing.

Of particular interest to Dr. Li Chi and his associates was the discovery that these Black Pottery People practiced the art of scapulimancy, a process of foretelling future events by the use of divination bones. Up to the time of the excavation of Ch'eng-tzu-yai, the use of divination or oracle bones had seemed to be confined, so far as was known, to the Shang City-State, for at that site bones had been found that were definitely identified as having been used for divination purposes in the practice of scapulimancy.

The bones found at Ch'eng-tzu-yai were all portions of the scapulae, or shoulder blade, of either oxen or deer, or in one instance the scapula of some other unidentified and probably wild creature, and they had all been prepared, though very crudely, to be used for divination purposes. The process was to scrape the bones thin and sink holes in the rough back sides of them so that when heat was applied at the point of boring, radial cracks would develop on the smooth front side. It was these cracks that were read by the soothsayers and interpreted to foretell the future. But compared with the oracle bones and turtle shells found at Anyang, the site of the Shang City-State, the specimens that Li Chi unearthed were very crude indeed. They were not scraped very thin or otherwise prepared with any great care, and since they showed so many borings—in one instance as many as one hundred forty-six on one half section of scapula, indicating it had been used that number of times for divination purposes—there was no room for characters to ask the questions that were to be answered by the oracles.

All this suggested that the practice of scapulimancy was in an early stage of development among the Black Pottery People. As a matter of fact, considering the borings and scorings and the cultural level at which the various pieces were found at Ch'eng-tzu-yai, it was believed that steps in the gradual evolution of scapulimancy could be traced toward the highest point of development as exemplified by the oracle bones that were found at Anyang. There they had been dug up in such numbers as to suggest the existence of temples which were actual repositories, where oracle bones were interpreted by priests and filed for the purposes of official record.

This theory, combined with other observations resulting from a careful and scholarly study of the artifacts collected from a number of Neolithic sites, is believed by some Sinologists to provide a partial answer to the question that interested Andersson. It will be remembered that when he discovered the Yang-shao Red (or painted) Pottery culture and noted some resemblances to pottery discovered in southeastern Europe and Eurasia, he felt that the art of making it might have been imported into China from the west. But after he had undertaken to trace the route of migration by which it might have entered China, with not too convincing results, he was no longer sure of his hypothesis. After Andersson, over the years, other Sinologists developed the theory that the reverse was possibly true and that there was an important cultural development in northeastern China which may well have spread westward. It was felt that the discoveries at Ch'eng-tzu-yai of the Black Pottery culture went a long way toward supporting this theory.

There are other scholars, however, who with more evidence to study feel that there were two distinct cultural traditions, one in the west of northern China and one in the east. Each in a measure expanded toward the other, though it is a question whether they ever really merged. Instead, the pottery seems to have changed, if not deteriorated, into coarse gray ceramics that spread over a wide area, both eastward and westward. The only form of decoration was the cord or mat pattern observed in some of the artifacts found in the upper cultural levels at Ch'eng-tzu-yai.

But then, with surprising suddenness, as far as the archeologists are concerned, appear the Shang-Yin people, who seem to emerge out of a period of complete darkness, historically speaking.

They bring with them the foundations of Chinese civilization, including the beginnings of organized government as well as a fully developed script that differs paleographically very little from the present calligraphy of the Chinese. They also created the beginnings of Chinese art reflected in their carvings of jade, bone, ivory and their rare stone sculpture, and above all in the beautiful bronzes that are so outstandingly a part of the Shang-Yin civilization. Indeed, these culturally well-advanced people seem to have emerged from a limbo of darkness with a thoroughly established bronze art that bespeaks generations, if not indeed centuries, of striving toward perfection. But a few of the steps in this upward progress have so far come to light anywhere else in China.

The nearest to anything that suggests origins in the Late Stone Age of the Bronze Age Shang-Yin people are the few bronze objects found at Ch'eng-tzu-yai, referred to earlier in this chapter. These and the crude evidence of the beginning of scapulimancy, which was later very much refined and developed by the Shang-Yin people, may well form a slight bridge across the dark chasm in the history of Chinese civilization.

But much more evidence and much deeper study is necessary to produce anything like a satisfactory picture, particularly from the point of view of the archeologists. As matters stand now, only the inscriptions on the thousands of oracle bones dug up at Anyang, which are believed to be part of the archives of the Shang-Yin City-State, do very much to eliminate the gloom of that abyss. And they leave much to be desired, though they are far more substantial than the legends on which Sinologists had to depend before the oracle bones came to their attention.

Oracle Bones 7

It was the Sinologists' interest in dragon bones that led to the discovery of the site of the Shang City-State at Anyang and the practice of divination of ancient emperors by means of oracle bones. For years, indeed probably for generations, the farmers in the vicinity of the unimportant little hamlet of Hsiao-t'un Ts'un, in the district of Anyang in the northern part of the province of Honan, noticed a strange phenomenon. With each thaw after a heavy freeze, or each spring plowing, or following heavy rainstorms, for some strange and mysterious reason, pieces of bone and turtle shells of various shapes and sizes would work their way up out of the ground. No one knows who was the first to pronounce them dragons' bones, but everyone knew that bones shed by dragons were supposed to have superior medicinal value. So the field workers gathered them and sold them to apothecary shops, or ground them up themselves into the fine powder known as the "knife point drug."

There were several local farmers who were especially talented at finding and unearthing these bone fragments and selling them to individuals and to the drugstore keepers in the nearby hamlet and in other sections of the district. In fact, one or two managed to make a living out of dragon bone digging and made some interesting finds, including bones that seemed to bear strange characters inscribed on them.

If the farmers ever wondered why some of the dragons' bones bore evidence of a quite ancient form of writing, there is no record that they ever said anything about it. As for the apothecaries themselves, just to keep the curious from asking questions, whenever they received dragon bones with inscriptions on them, they promptly erased them by grinding them off. Thus for years priceless information concerning what ultimately developed as one of the most colorful and most important archeological finds in the history of China was completely obliterated.

As far as is known, it was two scholarly gentlemen who had some knowledge of antique Chinese writing, Mr. Liu O and Mr. Wang I-jung, who first realized that some of the inscribed bones and shell fragments might have archeological value. Mr. Liu, on a visit to Peking, learned that his good friend, Mr. Wang I-jung, was ill and before leaving the capital he went to Wang's house to wish him a quick recovery. It happened that Wang was taking his medicine out of a turtle shell. Liu, watching the shell as Wang handled it, thought he saw vaguely recognizable antique characters scratched into the surface. He called Wang's attention to them and together they examined the shell closely, to discover what appeared to be a very old form of Chinese writing which they found interestingly difficult to decipher.

Both these gentlemen knew considerable about ancient Chinese history and they had, of course, read of the age-old custom of divination by means of turtle shells and oracle bones, though they knew little about the practice. The longer they studied these characters, the more they were convinced that they had stumbled on a clue that might lead to much more knowledge on the subject. Wang realized from his experience in studying characters that those on the turtle shell were of very great antiquity, and he worked hard at the task of trying to decipher them.

Also, as soon as he became well he visited the apothecary shop where he had procured the shell and began to ask questions concerning the part of the country from which it had come. With some reluctance the druggist told him that the residents of an area in Anyang, at a particular bend in the Huan River near the little community known as Hsiao-t'un Ts'un, dug these turtle shells and scraps of dragon bones from their cultivated fields. He said they worked at this during the winter, and each spring sold the bones for a few coppers to buyers from several drug supply houses. The price they received for them was very modest indeed, so Wang and Liu O made a tour of all the shops and, selecting those fragments on which the characters were quite clear, bought a number of them and returned home to study them seriously. They began to make real progress in interpreting the ancient writing, though they did not find this easy. Indeed, they encountered numerous difficulties, some of them insurmountable for that particular stage of their research.

Meanwhile, an ambitious curio merchant, one Fan Wei-ch'ing, also became interested in the bone and shell fragments, particularly when he learned that Wang I-jung was paying better prices for them than the drug dealers. So he proceeded to ferret out and buy the best pieces he could collect from the diggers.

He acquired quite a collection. Some of the best of these

he offered to Wang, quoting a price of two tael of silver for twelve particularly good specimens with inscriptions on them. The eagerness with which Wang purchased these inspired Fan to make even a larger collection, and in the spring of the following year he brought eight hundred fragments to Peking and sold them to the learned antiquarian who, with his good friend Liu O, was making a thorough study of the oracle bones, for this is what they were quite confident they had in their possession.

As a matter of fact, some inscriptions they were translating with difficulty not only established this fact to the satisfaction of Wang and Liu, but did more. They revealed to them that many of the questions asked of the oracles who manipulated the divinations were originally propounded by some of the kings of the ancient Shang dynasty. This harked back traditionally to the period between 1765 and 1123 B.C., and since up to that time very little if anything was known of Chinese history before the first millennium B.C., the information gleaned from the inscriptions on the bones was invaluable. Being questions of a type that would daily concern both kings and commoners, when they were interpreted they revealed fascinating pictures of the people of the ancient city-state and the way they thought and lived. Thus they furnished an insight into the Shang period more complete and more significant than would be possible through more deliberately historical documents.

The inscribed bones, through the medium of the oracle or diviner, furnished a way for the people of the Shang dynasty to consult with satisfying directness their gods and the spirits of their ancestors. This was highly important and a very comfortable way for them to conduct their affairs. The spirits

they thus communed with were at the same time most benevolent but very jealous. If they were properly consulted and if
they approved, they would give the project in question their
blessings and spiritual assistance. If, however, they were not
properly consulted or if they had not been satisfactorily pro-
pitiated with sacrifices of the kind they liked, their wrath
would be terrible to experience. For this reason, little indeed
was undertaken in those days until the spirits had been consulted by means of the oracle.

This was probably done in the temple dedicated to the
self-same ancestral spirits being importuned. Shells from a
type of land turtle long since extinct in China, and the shoulder blades or scapula or leg bones of cattle that had been
split and worked down to present a flat, polished surface were
used in the rites of divination. As far as is known, the question about which spiritual guidance was being sought would
be etched into the shell or bone with some sharp tool or
stylus, although the question was not always written down.
Then in some way, either with the glowing end of a stick or
a hot pebble or special instrument, heat would be applied to
a particular spot until cracks appeared on the opposite surface, and the way each crack radiated from the central point
was significant. Only the oracle priest could interpret these
cracks, of course, to give the answer to the person who waited
hopefully for the information. (See sketch.)

From shortly before the turn of the century when Liu O
and Wang I-jung began to give out information concerning
the oracle bones they had acquired, a torrid argument started
among the scholars as to the authenticity of these relics. A
majority insisted that they were spurious and that the legends
found on them were fakes. But they had good reason to feel
as they did because as soon as it was discovered collectors

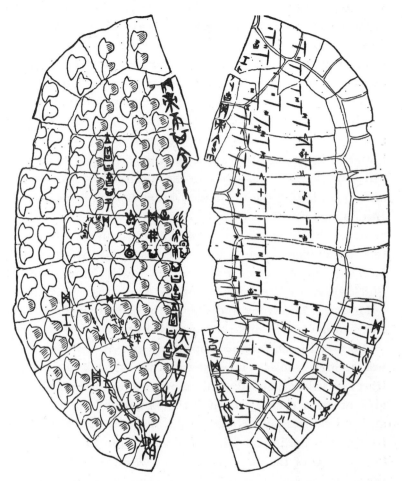

Sketch of turtle shell prepared for divination. Pits to receive heated implement (left-hand side); oracle cracks after heating (right-hand side). This shell was inscribed with characters on both the obverse and reverse sides, which is unusual. (Courtesy HJAS)

were willing to pay silver for these pieces of bone, several artists who were adept at counterfeiting them began to manufacture and sell them. Indeed, the business of making and selling oracle bones was carried on for years and many spurious ones found their way into now famous collections.

Mr. James Mellon Menzies, a Canadian missionary who lived near Hsiao-t'un, became interested in the oracle bones and proceeded to collect them. But one of the first ones he bought was an imitation done on the scapula of a recently killed ox. It wasn't long before the specimen began to ripen and smell, letting the missionary know he had been hoaxed. But by studying the fake and taking note of the fact that the genuine clearly reveal traces of mineral deposits which can only accumulate through long interment, Mr. Menzies, who later became quite an authority on oracle bones, learned quickly how to detect any counterfeits.

However, Mr. Wang and Mr. Liu insisted that theirs were the genuine article, and they stoutly defended their findings.

They had some valiant supporters, too. At any rate, there was enough scholarly interest to make them decide that at least one volume, and possibly more, should be published to give others a chance to study the bones and their curious antique calligraphy. About this time, however, the Boxer trouble was boiling over in China, and unfortunately Wang became one of the victims of Boxer wrath. Liu O survived the rebellion and went into the business of collecting oracle bones with renewed enthusiasm, with a book about them in the back of his mind.

Mr. Fan, because of the rebellion, was forced to flee to Shantung. He left his collection of bone and shell fragments in the hands of a fellow curio dealer, and ultimately these, about three hundred in number, came into the possession of

Liu O. He also acquired a thousand or more that had been owned by Wang I-jung and were sold by his son Wang Han-p'u to settle his father's estate and pay his debts. Liu O also hired Fan's friend, the curio dealer, one Chao Chih-chai, to work for him as a collector and sent him all through north China searching out oracle bones in the hands of apothecaries and collectors. By the end of the war period he had acquired more than three thousand pieces. At the same time one of Liu's sons had been collecting for him in the vicinity of Anyang and he brought back another thousand fragments.

Of this collection, then the largest extant, Liu O selected 1,058 of the best specimens, made rubbings of them and had them reproduced and printed by lithography. They appeared in six volumes under the title *T'ieh-yun Ts'ang-K'uei* (Turtle Shells from the Iron Cloud Studio) which was later referred to as *TYTK* and has the distinction of being the first published collection of oracle bone fragments, to which Lo Chen-yü wrote a discerning preface. Unfortunately, Liu O later became involved in some kind of official difficulty and was banished to Sinkiang, where he died. With his banishment his collection became badly scattered. Mr. Lo Chen-yü became the possessor of a number of the fragments, and another group was added to the collection of an Englishwoman of Shanghai named Mrs. Hardoon.

By this time many others were making collections of bone and shell fragments. Among them was the erudite Sun I-jang, who worked very hard at studying the inscribed oracle bones. Proficient in the beginning in the art of reading antique characters on bronzes, he made excellent progress when he undertook the study of oracle bone writing, and he was considered to be the pioneer in that field.

Lo Chen-yü, who wrote the preface to *TYTK*, was also an

ardent student of oracle bones, and it is said that after Sun I-jang none worked longer or contributed more to the study of these inscriptions than he. A Japanese scholar, one Mr. Hayashi, also made valuable contributions in this field of endeavor, as indeed did many others including the Canadian missionary, James Mellon Menzies, and Frank Chalfant and Roswell Britton, to mention only a few of the foreign epigraphers who have interested themselves in this work.

Of all the students who had a part in revealing the riddle of the discovery at Anyang, Dr. Tung Tso-pin ultimately, more than two decades later, became recognized as being the world's greatest authority on the inscriptions on the oracle bones.

It is a strange fact, however, that in spite of the enthusiasm of a few scholars in China and in other countries, very little general interest in the oracle bones and their significance developed over a period of years. It was recognized that the bones, besides supplying important information on the subject of scapulimancy, also revealed valuable facts on the previously little-known Shang City-State and at least ten different Shang kings. But strangely enough, no scientific effort was made to excavate the area at Anyang in which the oracle bones were found until almost three decades after they had first been brought to the attention of the world.

True, quite a number of collections of bone and small fragments were made by individuals, and many were sold to museums of the importance of the Carnegie Museum in Pittsburgh, the Royal Scottish Museum in Edinburgh, the British Museum, the Museum für Volkerkunde in Germany, the museum of the Anglo Chinese College in Tientsin, and several other institutions of similar importance. But no recognized digging was done at Anyang until 1928. Meanwhile,

word got around in the circle interested that the supply of
bones was fast being exhausted, which helped to increase the
price of specimens among collectors.

There was, however, quite a lot of unofficial, haphazard
digging going on at Anyang, with the result that a lot of
valuable archeological material was being destroyed or damaged. These efforts brought more and more oracle bones on
the market, belying the report that the treasury was empty.
Many of them were spurious, of course, for there were now
a number of accomplished counterfeiters at work and doing
very well indeed in the matter of prices they received for
their imitations.

So lucrative did the market for these fragments appear to
be that one of the village elders of Hsiao-t'un organized a
group of farmers and began an ambitious operation on the
south bank of the Huan River, north of the village itself.
Protected by matting, tents and braziers, they worked during
most of the cold weather and managed to unearth several
cartloads of oracle bones.

As was to be expected, there were some villagers who objected to the digging, and a wrangle over property rights and
privileges soon burst forth in an armed battle and terminated
in a lawsuit. However, all the newly discovered fragments
undoubtedly got into the market. And the upshot of the
disagreement was that the village officials prohibited further
excavation. This made little difference, for there were blithe
poachers who still made a living searching for these fragments
in spite of the ordinance against digging.

This local ordinance was the first evidence of government
recognition of the fact that some of the nation's most valuable archeological treasures were being destroyed. In truth,
highly important historical information was being irretriev-

ably lost because a few peasants saw in their haphazard digging a way of making a few extra coppers during the season
when they were not engaged in agriculture. So the prohibi-
tion against digging was an important step because it fitted
in with the efforts being made by the Academia Sinica and
other scholarly groups to organize a thoroughly scientific
investigation of the site on the banks of the Huan River and
start the first entirely Chinese dig at Anyang.

Dr. Tung Tso-pin was appointed to take charge of the preliminary investigation and excavation because of his exceptional knowledge of the Shang City-State, which he preferred
to call the Yin dynasty. He had established, through a very
precise study of thousands of these bits of bone, dates for
certain eclipses of both the sun and the moon. These celestial
events were always of such tremendous importance that the
Shang rulers requested supernatural guidance through the
medium of their diviners. Thus a relative chronology of
these events and the names of the Shang kings seeking information was compiled which helped Tung Tso-pin to formu-
late some order of succession and establish the time of certain
other contemporaneous events some three thousand years in
the past.

Tung, a graduate of Peking University and a Research
Fellow of the Academia Sinica, being so elected in 1948 in
Taiwan, was a visiting professor at Chicago University in
1947. Many former students there and at Yale, where he lec-
tured that same year, will remember him as a small, rather
slight man with a face that looked weather-beaten. He had a
wry sense of humor and a rueful smile. He was constantly
making subtle jokes with his associate, the late Lo Ch'ang-pei,
because the word for turtle, *wu-kuei*, is also an old-fashioned
term for cuckold. This presented humorous possibilities to

archeologists interested in turtles or turtle shells, and Tung frequently took advantage of the fact.

Being concerned over various reports about the disappearance of the oracle bones, Tung went to Anyang by rail, and immediately looked up his friend, Mr. Chang T'ien-chi, head of the Eleventh Provincial School in Honan. The principal had himself visited the area where the bones were found. It was located about one *li* (a third of a mile) north of the hamlet of Hsiao-t'un Ts'un, where there is a promontory at a bend in the Huan River. There the bones were discovered in the cultivated fields.

He said that he and his students had gone out there once and had seen bone fragments on the surface. The pedagogue had dug into the earth in one field with a stick and at the depth of about a foot, he had turned up a small bone fragment with a character sketched on it. He did not feel that there was any scarcity of these bones, and said any number could be bought in the town of Anyang. In fact, he assured Tung that if word got out he was looking for dragons' bones, the women and children would swarm around him trying to sell him what they had. He said he had bought a small basin full of them for one Mexican dollar quite recently, but had lost most of them during a bandit raid on the town. He also reported that year after year bones continued to appear above ground and that a friend of his had recently found an entire turtle shell.

Encouraged with this report, Tung decided to visit the area the next day. But heavy rain prevented this and he had to be content to go to Anyang and there visit the curio shops, of which there was an unusual number for a community of its size. And of course they all had oracle bones, or, rather, dragons' bones, for sale. Tung and the principal made a tour of these shops, most of which were on the main street, extending from the north gate to the drum tower. They examined many bone fragments, some with characters on them and some without any. Many were genuine, but there were also many that were spurious. However, when Tung and his companion asked questions about them and inquired about where and when they had been found, the curio dealers were once more blandly ignorant. Tung said he could detect the fact that the dealers knew they were outsiders and did not intend to give them any information whatever. All of this gave Tung a growing feeling that he was on the trail of a great discovery, but even he never guessed its importance.

They finally ran across a dealer named Mr. Wang in an alley by the bell tower who had a good collection of oracle bones and who was forthright and honest and in no way reluctant to give them information. He said a great many oracle bones had come to light in recent years following the heavy frosts or heavy rains and that there did not seem to be any scarcity of them. Tung and his friend looked over the bones he had with characters on them which Wang assured them were genuine. He also showed them some imitation oracle bones, and even a most casual comparison between the genuine and the spurious made it evident which were the bogus ones. The characters etched on them, besides lacking the evidence of having been buried for a long period, also were crudely made. Some were turned upside down, or were improperly drawn, and half of them made no sense to the experienced collector.

The next day, with clear weather, Tung and his friend Mr. Chang walked the railroad tracks and cart ruts to Hsiao-t'un. Here they found no dearth at all of bone fragments. Every house in the village had great batches of them, and women

and children swarmed around them trying to sell bone fragments. These villagers did not hesitate to say that everyone
dug for dragon bones whenever he got a chance and that it
was here to their village that the curio dealers and many of
the drug houses came to replenish their stock.

With this evidence that the supply of oracle bones was as
plentiful as he had hoped, Tung and Mr. Chang became eager
to try their own luck at digging for them. But at this they
were at first conspicuously unsuccessful though they hired
several natives to show them the best places to conduct their
operations, and devised ingenious plans for their explorations. Because he realized that irreplaceable archeological
treasures were being destroyed by all the amateur digging
that had been going on for years and was still being done,
Dr. Tung decided to try to enlist the cooperation and friendly
interest of all the scholarly organizations of the country in
his endeavors.

With this in mind, he journeyed to Shanghai, where he met
Dr. Fu Ssu-nien, the head of the Academia Sinica, who was
staying at a hotel there. After listening to Dr. Tung's report
on the situation at Anyang, Dr. Fu was convinced of the
desirability of the Academia Sinica taking on the responsibility for the excavation. He promptly arranged for an ap-
propriation of one thousand dollars, Mexican, for the
purchase of surveying and photographic equipment. He arranged with the Governor of Honan Province to send assistance and to permit the use of soldiers from the garrison at
Anyang to protect the workmen from bandit raids. Dr. Fu
also enlisted the interest and assistance of the Commissioner
for the Preservation of Relics and appointed Mr. Li Ch'un-yü
as surveyor and photographer.

And in order to put an end to the haphazard digging of

the peasants, which bothered Dr. Tung so much, he pursuaded the authorities to issue a strict ordinance that there should be no more individual digging in the Anyang area. This, however, had a startling repercussion, for when Tung got back with his assistants and began to organize his efforts, he found himself confronted by the directive he had had issued. For a time he was faced with a dilemma of his own making, and it required some effort to get things straightened out.

When they finally convinced the headman of the village, Chang Hsüeh, that all was in order and that they had official permission to excavate, he was very cooperative. He helped organize a party of fifteen diggers equipped with tools, windlasses and earth-carrying baskets, called out twelve members of the citizens' militia as guards, and the work finally got under way. Mr. Chang had also announced that any crops destroyed by the digging would be paid for and all holes or trenches dug would be filled in before the dig was over, which made the peasants feel a little happier about the whole thing.

These details all arranged and several changes made in his plans for digging, Dr. Tung's operation was started with the hopes of everyone quite high at the beginning. They began to dwindle, however, for the digging was hard and slow and the results meager indeed. Trench after trench was started and abandoned in several different locations, but aside from some mutilated pieces of bronze and a few bone fragments of little value, nothing was found. Low of spirit and with everyone nursing tired backs, the work was carried on with dwindling enthusiasm for several days. As a matter of fact, it was not until they obtained permission to dig on the property of one Mr. Lu, where a workman reported having found a piece of bone with characters on it some time previous, that everyone took heart once more. In this new area trench No. 36 as well as four supplementary trenches were opened up.

It was trench No. 36 which produced the relics that made all previous efforts well worthwhile and resulted in the assertion by Dr. Tung that the first dig at Anyang in the fall of 1928, after a very disappointing start, finished up a complete success. Digging in this new area started on the twenty-third of October, but the weather gave every indication that the period of comfortable digging would be terminated by fall storms at any time. The big trench developed in the shape of a crude boomerang and finally extended twenty-two feet in length, varying from two to five feet in width.

It was not long after the trench got started that the yellow loess began to give way to darker earth, and presently the diggers reached what Dr. Tung realized was really a culture layer. Fine specimens of oracle bones, most of them good-sized, and of turtle shell began to appear, to the manifest enthusiasm of everyone. This was what they had been hoping and working for these many days past, and to be thus finally rewarded excited everyone down to the most phlegmatic digger. Eagerly they followed this cultural layer down to a depth of fifteen feet, and in the process they found one hundred thirty-five pieces of oracle bones, which was indeed a rich find, considering the meager results from all the previous trenches.

As was feared, the digging had to be brought to a finish four days later. On the thirtieth of October, in increasingly bad weather, the trenches were filled in, the men were paid off and dismissed, and the first scientifically organized exploration of the Shang City-State site was brought to an end. Dr. Tung, naturally, was very pleased with the report he was able to make, and so too were the officials of the Academia

Sinica and the other organizations associated with the work. Tung and some other scientists had the feeling that perhaps their efforts had indeed resulted in locating what might have been the original repository of all the oracle bones as well as the site of the City Shang for which he had been searching. They had high hopes that future excavations would result in some spectacular revelations regarding the early civilization of China.

Answers 8
from Anyang

The Chinese insist that theirs is the oldest civilization in the world. They point to legends and traditions that reach far back into prehistory and tell tales of fabulous emperors who performed tremendous deeds and achieved mighty triumphs over nomadic barbarians who attacked their ancient cities. But unfortunately there has been no more reliable evidence to support their contentions than the legends of these fictitious heroes.

The truth of the matter is that until the oracle bones were discovered at Anyang and their importance in revealing the history of the Shang City-State appreciated, there was very little known of the culture of China earlier than the ninth century before the Christian era.

To be sure, the diligence and painstaking efforts of Dr. Andersson and his confreres established many things about Peking man and his primitive Early Stone Age culture. These scientists have revealed to us through their astute studies that the progeny of *Sinanthropus Pekinensis* made slow but steady progress in many directions. We know they improved their crude stone weapons and ultimately developed the composite reflex bow, a superior type of distinctively Mongolian origin. They domesticated animals, the pig first, then the dog, and much later sheep, oxen, horses, poultry. They learned farming, too, and added grain and other agricultural products to a food supply that was chiefly derived from hunting and fishing.

We also know that when agriculture became more reliable than hunting for the sustenance of growing groups of people, they moved out of the caves to the edges of the broad plains areas. And possibly because they had become accustomed to living in caves, and because these extensive grasslands were comparatively treeless, they developed a type of dwelling that was in effect a circular dugout with a storage pit for a cellar, with a hard-packed earthen floor and which was, of course, roofed over. Somewhat similar dwellings with sod roofs were the abodes of our frontiersmen of the plains states in the early eighteen hundreds.

The peculiar ability of the yellow loess soil to stand in high cut banks without collapsing, lent itself well to this type of dwelling, and the Chinese domicile of Neolithic culture, evolved with some modification and improvement, is still used today in many sections of China. These dugout dwellings were constructed so as to compose well-knit communities which were surrounded with walls of pounded earth, often packed so hard that traces of them are still to be found after thousands of years of rain and erosion.

Forced by changing weather conditions and extreme hardships, which probably included a dwindling food supply, scientists tell us that these people began, sometime after the last glacial period, a slow migration in many directions. Ultimately, some of them found a land bridge to North America, which to many anthropologists explains some of the noticeable similarities in the culture of the American Indians and the Neolithic people of China. This migration has been established by more than just the evidence detected through cultural comparisons, however, for it has been more or less determined that the American Indian came originally from Mongoloid stock. The skulls that have been studied reveal much telltale evidence of Mongolian origin. Not the least of this is the presence of shovel-shaped incisors, a hallmark of the Sino-Asiatic people.

Those who were the ancestors of the Chinese of today we know began to develop crafts many centuries before their known history begins. From shells gathered from rivers and fresh-water lakes they evolved the art of making a number of useful implements and ornamental trinkets. One of their outstanding achievements in craftsmanship was the making of pottery. It was crude at first and of a dull gray color, sometimes with ornamental designs pressed into the surface. But probably because they were naturally an artistic people and found pleasure in creating beautiful things, the quality and appearance of their pottery grew increasingly more attractive.

Soon they began to make it thinner and of more graceful design. They learned how to decorate it with paint, creating remarkably beautiful patterns, first in monochrome, mostly red, then in a variety of colors. Artifacts of the painted pottery culture era in China testify that these people were farther advanced in color and design than any other Neolithic people.

Not only were the decorative qualities outstandingly attractive, but the structural design of the pottery, besides having utilitarian value, was remarkably flowing in form. They created beautiful basins, urns, bowls, pots, jugs, and several cooking utensils found nowhere among people of that era save in China. The most notable of these is the *li,* a pottery tripod vessel with hollow legs in which, if desired, three different foods could be cooked at one time, with all of them receiving the same comparative amount of heat. This unique utensil was found by Dr. Andersson already developed to its present stage, as the reader will recall, among the Yang-shao people of the Painted Pottery culture.

It has been suggested that these interesting cooking utensils were devised through the prevailing habit of leaning three vessels with round or pointed bottoms against each other for support over the cooking fires. From this, some prehistoric inventors conceived the idea of making the three into one utensil in tripod form. They also developed a progressive type of a *li* tripod known as a *hsien.* This provided for a pottery bowl-shaped top having a bottom filled with holes so that steam could pass through. It fitted snugly on top of a tripod base, and when water was put in the hollow legs of the bottom receptacle and boiled, steam would pass through the top container and cook the food there, steaming it in much the same fashion employed by the Chinese today. It is also believed that somewhere about this period they developed the potter's wheel, which helped to account for the fine quality of their pottery.

They evolved a system of picture writing, too, but how and when this developed will probably never be known. There really isn't any indication that this had taken place before the second millennium B.C. In fact, the earliest evidence of Chinese writing is that found on the oracle bones of the Shang people at Anyang, but this is so well advanced that it bespeaks an evolution that had unquestionably gone on through many centuries.

But because early records were written on silk or bamboo or some other perishable material, and apparently no effort was made to preserve them, practically all historical documents of early China have disappeared. Indeed, until the oracle bones were discovered and efforts made to study and interpret them, there was, as has been mentioned before, no reliable way (save by bronze inscriptions) of learning anything of Chinese history before about 1000 B.C. There was, to be sure, a wealth of tradition, lore and mythology that built a picture of a succession of emperors and kings extending far back into antiquity but becoming badly scrambled with legends and the supernatural. Obviously very little of this can be depended upon as reliable.

There has been much told and written about what was considered to be the first of the ruling dynasties of China, known as the Hsia. According to the best information available, in documents that do not always support each other, sometime during the period between 2205 and 1994 B.C., a dynasty came into existence that lasted for five or six centuries.

Tradition has it that they were a progressive people who collected in city-states ruled by a succession of monarchs of heroic stature who fostered industries and crafts of a nature so advanced that they suggest many centuries of development. Tradition has it also that they had long used the wheel, both on war chariots and in agriculture; that they had developed silkworm culture and the art of fine weaving; that they had an exceptional knowledge of the art of working with bronze. They are said to have had a fully developed system of writing which, like many other things, implied a background of many generations of tradition.

It was among the Hsia that much of the colorful lore of the dragons is said to have originated, to be carried down the ages with considerable embellishment, of course. One of the ancestors of the Hsia, in order to achieve grace and to establish himself as one who was empowered to rule, is said to have changed himself into a dragon after he had been cut up into small pieces (by whom, no one knows). Upon ascending the throne, he adopted the dragon as the symbol of royalty, and some of his kinsmen were given the right to breed dragons, which they are said to have done with great success. One of the kings of the Hsia is pictured as feeding on the flesh of dragons to augment his royal wisdom and kingly justice, according to another oft-told legend.

And yet, strangely enough, all that proves the existence of the Hsia are these same traditions and legends that tell of fabled dragons. Some scholars contend that the people who were responsible for the Yang-shao painted pottery were actually the remnants of the Hsia. And there are others who believe that those who were responsible for the Black Pottery of the Shantung Province were descended from these legendary people. But in neither case is there strong proof, so, unless the Communists, who say they have 25,000 archeologists digging like mad, have been able to locate sites in some of the cities in which the Hsia are supposed to have lived, there is nothing reliable, such as inscribed bronzes, oracle bones, pottery or weapons, to furnish a record of these people and the high culture it is said they must have enjoyed.

But, of course, that was in a measure true of the Shang City-State until there was a more intensive study of the oracle bones found at Anyang after nearly thirty years of neglect by the Chinese archeologists themselves. So perhaps someday as much will be known about the Hsia as we now know about the Shang-Yin people, thanks to the curiosity and persistence of many scholars, not the least among them being Dr. Tung Tso-pin.

It is true that Dr. Tung's enthusiasm was drained to such a low point that it almost disappeared toward the end of the first dig on the Anyang site. Had it not been for the very fortunate discovery of 135 excellent specimens of oracle bones in the thirty-sixth and last trench they planned to dig that year, it is possible that Hsiao-t'un might have been abandoned as the likely site of the Shang-Yin capital and not explored again for a long time.

As with the Hsia, by legend and tradition, a great deal was heard about the Great City Shang. The oracle bones and some bronzes that had been studied since the days of Mr. Wang I-jung added considerably more to the existing knowledge about the Shang-Yin culture. For one thing, they seemed to point to the fact that the hamlet of Hsiao-t'un and the surrounding area near Anyang on the banks of the Huan River was the site of the Shang-Yin capital city, though there were some who refused to accept this at first.

However, the one hundred thirty-five specimens of oracle bones and turtle shell fragments found by Dr. Tung on the last day of their dig in October 1928 went a long way toward confirming the theory of the location of the Shang City site in that place. They also helped dispel in some quarters the idea that these bones were forgeries and that the supply had been exhausted by the destructive, indiscriminate digging by the natives of the area. So it was with renewed enthusiasm that the digging was started again the following spring.

Indeed, the encouragement engendered by Tung's finds

stimulated the interest of American archeologists, among them Mr. Carl Bishop of the Freer Gallery of Art and the Smithsonian Institution and his former associate, Dr. Li Chi. For some time they had contemplated excavating the Anyang site, and they finally decided to join forces with the National Research Institute of China, to begin excavating on a considerably larger scale than had been carried on by Tung. They planned to dig for two months in the spring and two months in the fall with a large force of workmen.

But again results were slow in developing. More pits were sunk in the vicinity of trench No. 36 and the four shorter lateral trenches without producing any hopeful results. Then the archeologists moved to an area north of the town and began to work in the fields but without very much greater success, though they did make one find that proved to be important later on. An object that after some study was characterized as a sectioned mold used in the casting of bronze was unearthed, which indicated quite clearly that artisans who knew how to work in metal had been part of the town at one time. This in turn suggested that they were digging into the site of a large community, probably a Bronze Age city, which added to the conviction some of the archeologists had that somewhere under the surface in that vicinity were indeed the remains of the capital city of the Shang-Yin people.

The results of these efforts in the north fields were meager and the area was soon abandoned. Then, after trying again with little result to the east of the productive trench No. 36, the discouraged archeologists and their workers were driven back to the village of Hsiao-t'un. There they got the inspiration to dig under an area almost in the heart of the community known as the threshing floor, named for the obvious reason that it was where at harvest time the peasants brought

that manpower could exert. This and timber brought out of the nearby mountains served their most demanding construction needs and for their purposes were apparently very satisfactory. Indeed it is known they erected structures more than one hundred feet long in the Shang-Yin capital.

Temples and the dwellings of the officials and more important Shang people were built on terraces or platforms of this pounded earth, with timbered pillars supporting gabled roofs. From characters found on the oracle bones it was quite clear that the structures of the Shang era were much the same as the Chinese buildings of today except for the present use of brick and roof tiles. The roofing material of the Shang period must have been rush thatching and mud, and the sidewalls probably were mere screens made of various materials, almost as perishable as rush thatching. For that reason, all that could be found of the buildings of the one-time Great City Shang, as it was referred to in legends of the ancient capital, were the pounded earth platforms and occasional charred evidence of the timbered pillars with the stone or bronze foundations that were placed under them to keep them from sinking into the ground.

Although Li Chi and his associates worked hard to try to get a clear idea of the cultural layer of the earth at the time of the City Shang, before the flood or floods had deposited heavy layers of silt there, they found it very difficult to make many positive observations. The earth in the area of the threshing floor was badly disturbed, indeed bafflingly scrambled. The condition was the same in all the trenches. The result was that no traces of the temple they felt should have been there could be found, nor could they locate, at that time, many definite indications that they were digging in the heart of the ancient city.

Dr. Li Chi felt that fairly frequent floods had inundated that big bend in the Huan River, eroding the original surface and possibly exposing so many oracle bones that the natives had been encouraged to dig there for some time even before 1899, when the first-known collections of bone fragments came into the market. He also suggested that perhaps the Chinese farmers, having no water nearer than the river, had been for the last four centuries digging wells in that area from which they drew water to irrigate their fields. This was done by the laborious process of carrying it in buckets, so the nearer their wells were to their fields, the better.

Also the farmers had a great habit of borrowing earth from one area to help level off a cultivated field then in use close at hand. And, of course, the indiscriminate digging of dragon bone hunters and grave robbers had added to the chaotic condition of the terrain. Altogether, it was an almost impossible task to unscramble the jumbled earth and reconstruct the cultural level.

The archeologists felt, however, that, in spite of dangers of floods and the devastation they caused, there had been a succession of communities at that bend of the Huan River. They were believed to begin back in a period even before the Shang City-State and to continue intermittently right up until the present, for there was a busy and thriving little village there at the time the digging was in operation.

During this second dig in 1929, one of the important finds was a sherd of crude painted pottery which was identified as being of the Yang-shao type. The people who made this pottery, as we know, were Neolithic men of the Painted Pottery culture extant many centuries before the Shang people, and this sherd suggested that there had been a village of them there long before the Shangs moved in.

It developed later that there had been a village of Painted Pottery People on a bend in the Huan River downstream from the Anyang site, too. So it was reasonable to suppose that there had also been one at the Hsiao-t'un bend, since it was a better location for a village. Later there was discovered evidence of the fact that the Neolithic people of the Black Pottery culture had supplanted the Painted Pottery People and had a community on the lower bend from which they in turn were driven by the Shangs. And there was evidence that following the Shangs the site had been used again and again by people of later ages.

Tombs were found which proved the area where excavation was being done had been used as a burial ground by the people of many different dynasties. Although most of the tombs had long since been looted by grave robbers, and all the funerary furniture, such as bronze urns and the like, had been removed, there still remained sufficient evidence, including inscriptions, to identify them as being from several different eras. The archeologists were certain, for instance, that there had been a village there and that burials had been made during the Ming dynasty, which ended in A.D. 1644.

They also found tombs of much earlier periods such as the T'ang dynasty extant between 618 and 905 A.D. It is probable that these villages were from time to time devastated by floods too, but their end more likely came about when they were attacked by stronger invading forces who confiscated their treasures, burned their villages and enslaved their inhabitants.

There is abundant evidence that the Neolithic people who inhabited the village at the bend of the river downstream from the Anyang site were attacked by invaders and that they put up a desperate fight to drive them off. Evidence of the pounded earthen wall that had been erected as a defense against attackers was found, and the presence of an amazing number of arrowheads and other kinds of weapons testified to the terrific battle or battles that had taken place there. Efforts were made to locate the wall that the archeologists felt certain must have been part of the defenses of the Shang-Yin capital, but they were unable to find it during any of the later digs.

Indications of the succession of villages that had been built on the Shang City site, right down to the village which existed there while the excavation was being carried on almost under the houses, led to some interesting speculation. Why did successive generations of people insist on maintaining villages at that particular spot? Conquerors came, the village was devastated, probably burned, and general destruction was wreaked on the place, but soon it was rebuilt. Was it re-established because the site was a good one on a promontory easily defended, with the river forming a natural moat and only a short defensive wall was required? Or did superstition or tradition motivate the reconstruction efforts of the people? Though the archeologists worked hard, they never could be entirely sure of the answer to these questions.

The fact that the tombs of their ancestors were located there may have had something to do with the desires of the people to cling to the original village site. It is true that many of the tombs uncovered during the excavation at the Anyang site had been ruthlessly looted. But this was probably done by later generations of villagers. It seems very unlikely that the tombs were disturbed by the people of the same dynasty because of the reverence and superstitious fear in which the spirits of the dead were held.

And yet, strangely enough, this fear of the supernatural

was not a sufficient deterrent to keep the peasants of any generation from grave robbing, for in many places in China this form of vandalism, along with banditry, developed to the point of becoming a vocation. There has always been a strong superstition among the Chinese people that disturbing ancestral graves would bring about disasters in many horrible forms. It was well known that the spirits of the dead when disturbed grew angry and vindictive and often vented their wrath on a whole community, and there were laws evolved that provided for ruthless punishment for the crime of grave robbing, such as slicing the culprit into thin strips—while he was still alive! But in spite of these laws and the ill luck that might befall them, the peasants in areas like Anyang, where ancient tombs and burial grounds were known to exist, supported more than one ghoulish group constantly on the lookout for graves that might be opened up in a nocturnal venture.

Unlike the stone and brick tombs of the Near East, the Chinese tombs were made of pounded earth, similar to the walls and the building foundations of the community. Entering them was merely a matter of digging, once one was located, then tunneling around the area until the bronzes and all the other valuables that had been buried there were found and sent to the surface. The grave robbers devised ingenious methods of probing beneath the surface until they located the layer of hard earth that indicated a tomb had been found. One single grave of a king or a person of high degree could easily make all the robbers wealthy. But the ghouls would never leave the tomb they had rifled until they had scattered all the bones of the corpses so they never could be reorganized. In this way it was believed any vengeance the spirits of the departed might undertake would be thwarted.

These grave robbers naturally resented the activities of the archeologists, and scientific excavating was not without its dangers. The ghouls were usually armed and they had few compunctions when it came to shooting a man. As a matter of fact, in many provinces and particularly in the vicinity of Anyang, these same men were likely to double as bandits at the slightest opportunity, raiding a village or an archeologist's camp and making off with all the treasure they could gather. They would take hostages, too, and hold them for a ransom, so for that reason, as was mentioned, no scientific excavating was carried on without a sizable bodyguard of soldiers to protect the archeologists and the diggers.

Dr. Li Chi and his assistants were deeply disappointed to find that so many of the Shang tombs they exposed as they worked down through the various strata had been visited by vandals before they got there. Most of them had been thoroughly looted of everything of value on which the grave robbers could hope to realize even a few coppers. And some of the treasures they found were undoubtedly very valuable both intrinsically and from a scientific standpoint.

But they could have been much more helpful in rolling back the curtains of history if they had been found and exhumed under proper scholarly direction and observation. As a matter of fact, a number of beautiful and valuable bronzes had been mysteriously appearing in the curio shops of Peking, Nanking and various other large cities over the previous decade. There was little information about where they came from or who found them, but as a result of the looted graves Dr. Li Chi and his associates found at the Anyang site in the spring and fall of 1929, the scientists felt quite certain they knew where some of these treasures had been dug up.

They found some relics that had been missed, of course,

and some graves that had been undisturbed because they were excavating on a much larger scale than the peasants and considerably larger than Dr. Tung and his diggers had operated when they did their exploring. In truth, the two 1929 digs could be considered a success, for they turned up artifacts and funeral furniture that proved beyond a doubt they were working in the area which had indeed been a capital of the Shang dynasty. Dr. Li Chi also was confident that future excavating efforts would probably turn up much valuable information about the people of that particular civilization, as well as those who preceded and followed them.

So the excavating work during 1929 came to an end in the fall with everyone feeling that more lay ahead and that work the following year might produce discoveries of inestimable archeological value, particularly if grave robbers could be restrained by the authorities of the central government. There was just one uncertainty in every one's mind, and that was the growing civil war.

There had been troop movements and fighting in the general vicinity of Anyang. Unfortunately, this continued to develop over the winter, until by spring it became very evident that any archeological efforts would be foolhardy. So, unhappily, further work at the site of the capital of the Shang City-State had to be postponed indefinitely. There appeared to be little chance, indeed, of excavation being resumed in 1930 anyway.

The Tombs   9
at Hsiao-t'un

Dr. Li Chi's fear that unsettled political conditions and the consequent troop movements and skirmishes
would make further explorations at Anyang extremely hazardous were well founded. Nevertheless, the men from Academia Sinica mounted seven exploration efforts at Anyang
before 1932. These digs were all reported in the four volumes
of *Anyang Fachüeh Paokao* (Reports on Excavation at Anyang). There were no reports, however, published from 1932
until 1947, so very little was known of the last eight digs,
which were completed between 1933 and 1937, when internal
troubles gave way to the attacks of Japan.

Few eras in history can equal in complexity or in numbers
of alarms and excursions the period between 1932 and 1937
in China. It was a time of war lords, bandits, sensational
coups d'état and unrelenting pressure from Japan, bent on
empire. That a peaceful and contemplative pursuit such as
archeology should flourish during this time seemed unlikely.
And yet it did.

During 1935 an American scholar, Dr. H. G. Creel, prowled through warehouses full of the treasure-trove from Hsiao-t'un. He walked in and out among the sites and the men who were digging and sweating where once the Shang people had trod. And often enough at night, when he had retired to write up his notes by the light of a smoky oil lamp, he could hear shots and flurries of conflict outside the walls of Anyang. The book Dr. Creel published in 1937, *The Birth of China,* was the first widely read work which used the information uncovered at Anyang.

But while the organized and large-scale operations were going on just north of the little village of Hsiao t'un in 1933, another smaller, unsanctioned but highly enterprising operation was taking place almost under the noses of the men from Academia Sinica. Across the river from the main site a group of Chinese, working at night and in secret, dug out a half dozen bronze vessels and much other material from a site which is now called the "elephant tomb" because elephants figured largely in the decorations on the bronzes which were exhumed. Few people even knew of the existence of this tomb until W. C. White published pictures and text in the *London Illustrated News* during March, April and May of 1935.

Because events were moving swiftly between 1932 and 1937 and publication lagged far behind, little reliable and scholarly information was to be had on later excavations of the Shang capital until after World War II, when Dr. Shih Chang-ju wrote up the summary of excavations eight through fifteen and published it in the *Journal of Chinese Archeology* which appeared in 1947. In this article is a curious example of how slowly information circulated during the period 1932 to 1947—a span of almost sixteen years.

Liang Ssu-yung and a small party of workers in 1937 began exploratory digging in a small knoll known by the villagers as Hou-Kang, or literally, "the hill behind the village." Only a stone's throw from the railroad, Dr. Tung Tso-pin had marked it from the train window the very first time he rode into Anyang, and always intended to explore it but never did. Here Liang and his men soon uncovered the evidence that showed the Painted Pottery People had settled along the Huan before the Black Pottery People arrived. The significance of this was at once understood, of course, but they also uncovered some mysterious circles, about ten feet across, which had been carefully coated with white lime plaster. In the center of these (and there were more than twenty of them found) like a raised black bull's-eye in a white target there was a round, blackened, circular surface of extremely hard fired clay. The men mused on these for days, and when they carefully cut through several to see how they were constructed, they were more perplexed than ever because they found that before the lime plaster had been spread, a rather careful foundation for it had been laid consisting of brownish earth mixed with straw. When this had been smoothed out, the plaster was spread on the surface. At the outer rim of the big circles they could see where the plaster was curved up so that the whole area was like a very flat white dish with edges slightly raised and then, apparently, broken off all the way round.

"We cannot say for sure, of course [wrote Liang], but I feel that these 'white limed surfaces' are connected with the superstitions or religion of the Black Pottery People. The raised and fired centers of them make one think of a place for a 'fire god.' Perhaps they were primitive altars to Heaven of which the Royal Temple of Heaven in Peking (also circular, with a central altar) is only the latest descendant."

In Shih Chang-ju's 1947 summary report he still speaks of these lime-plaster areas as "white limed surfaces." His phrasing leaves no doubt that their use or meaning was unknown to him when he wrote the 1947 report. Yet in 1935 Liu Yao had excavated quite a rich Neolithic site at Ta-lai Tien in Honan and found an incomplete "white limed surface," about which he had this to say in his report:

"The construction was all but identical with the surfaces discovered at Hou-kang; the very thin plaster coating over the layer of earth and straw mixed were the same. Atop the surface were found fragments of Black Pottery and in the under layer of straw and earth we found small broken pieces of Yang-shao pottery. Neither our find nor the sites at Hou-kang showed any vestiges of the circular wall that should have been there, so we had no way of knowing what these circles were. But in the winter of 1934, Mr. Hsu Hsu in Paochi Hsien, Shensi Province, had found these circles in their original state and they proved to be nothing more nor less than the plastered floor of the Black Pottery People's dwelling pits. The raised, blackened and fired circle in the middle was the family hearth."

So the mystery of the white circles had been solved by 1936, and yet a person reading Shih Chang-ju's article of 1947 could only assume that they were still a puzzle. All this, of course, makes it evident that the free exchange of information and a healthy rate of publication is as important to archeology as it is to any other intellectual endeavor. Fortunately for our knowledge of the spread of Neolithic people throughout China, this lag was made up and recognition of these limed floors for what they really were helped lead to understanding the very complex question of the relations between Black Pottery (Lung-shan) and Painted Pottery (Yang-shao) cultures. For these curiously neat white floors became one of the hallmarks which could be used to trace Lung-shan settlements.

The last qualified person to see the site of the City Shang before the clouds of World War II obscured all of that area of China arrived in 1939—two years after the last organized excavation had been carried out at Hsiao-t'un. He was Dr. S. Howard Hansford, presently head of the Percival David Foundation of Chinese Art at the University of London, who had accepted an invitation from the pastor of the Canadian Mission at Anyang to visit him and spend a few days at Hsiao-t'un to observe what was going on there. Mr. Hansford and his wife accepted and proceeded to make the journey from Peking, where he was writing his book on jade, to Anyang by rail at great risk to their own safety.

The railroad was in the hands of the Japanese and every station was a little fortress with machine guns mounted and ready for action, and the whole right-of-way was patrolled constantly. Trenches and barbed-wire entanglements were everywhere and there were armored trains and batteries of searchlights at important points along the line. The engine of the Hansfords' train shoved two flat cars ahead of it. They were loaded with sandbags so that if the tracks had been mined by the guerrilla fighters, as they often were, these flat cars would explode the mines, and the locomotive would not be injured.

Indications of savage clashes with the Japs were evident on every hand—trains had been wrecked and telegraph lines torn down. The Hansfords realized that they were constantly in grave danger not only from the Japanese who questioned them belligerently many times during the trip, but from the distrustful Chinese soldiers as well.

However, with some unpleasant moments, they finally reached the mission at Anyang and next day drove out to see the famous archeological site at Hsiao-t'un. This had been one of their ambitions ever since they had been in China. When the little motorcar in which they rode trundled into the village, the place looked completely deserted. All the population had quietly faded indoors because they were afraid that the strangers had something to do with the Japanese invaders. But when it became evident that they were not Japanese, everyone became friendly and proceeded to sell them all kinds of Shang-Yin relics.

Evidences of treasure hunting were to be seen on every side. Indeed, the earth in the narrow streets, in the dooryards to the houses and almost everywhere they looked showed signs of having been drilled by the busy earth augers which, as mentioned before, the Chinese call *t'an ch'iao*. These were drills mounted on long shafts which were worked into the earth and rotated until they had acquired a core of soil which was brought to the surface and examined. If this proved to be "pounded earth," of which the tombs were built, or if bits of pottery or some other artifacts were brought up, trenches were immediately started and a treasure search was on.

"When a really important bronze is dug up in the Anyang sites," wrote Professor Hansford in his article "A Visit to Anyang," "the farmer on whose land the find has been made sends word to a dealer in the city. The dealer goes out to the village, where a conference is held with all the parties who took part in the dig and have an interest in the find. After hours, perhaps days, of negotiation a price is agreed on and paid. But agreement is reached more quickly than it other-

wise might be owing to the difficulty of protecting a valuable
find, which is fair game for the more desperate and adven-
turous lads of the neighborhood villages.

"Then comes the hazardous business of taking the piece to
Peking or some city where the dealer can get the handsome
profit to which he considers the risk entitles him. His real
danger in 1939 was the rapacity of the Japanese soldiery,
from the highest officer down to the rank and file. Accordingly, a find was rarely taken into the city where it would
have to pass Japanese sentries at the gate. The railway, too,
was avoided because all the Chinese passengers were searched
by Japanese soldiers when they joined the train and when
they left it. So the thing would be taken on foot or in farm
carts from place to place, passing through many hands till it
reached its destination."

The Hansfords were also able to see the slightly sunken
outlines of many of the royal tombs that had been opened
and explored and filled up again. Professor Hansford recalled
that by great good fortune the scientists had been able to
locate this huge burial area; a necropolis near the village of
Hou-chia Chuang (see Map 2) that contained a number of
undoubted royal tombs that had not been completely dese-
crated by grave robbers of former generations and were sufficiently undisturbed to be opened and studied carefully.

Unfortunately, however, one of the largest and what
probably was the tomb of the most important person buried
there had already been found and plundered as early as the
sixth century A.D. At that time a shaft had been dug into the
Shang tomb from what had then been the surface and in
the deposits on top of this shaft, through which the tomb had
been robbed, a tomb of the Sui dynasty (581-618) had been
built. The large Shang tomb when it was explored by the

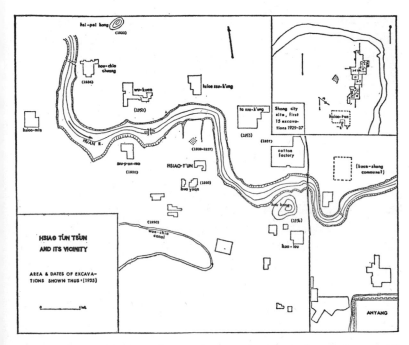

Map No. 2, showing the various excavations in and around Hsiao-t'un Ts'un giving dates. Other digs have been conducted here by the Communists but, as is to be expected, only the vaguest and most incomplete information concerning their results has trickled through the bamboo curtain.

archeologists was found to contain nothing but pebbles and a few potsherds.

From these tombs a rather complete picture of the contents of a grave of a nobleman or other person of importance could be developed. Of first interest, of course, was the contents of the huge casket containing the body of the deceased. There was always a variety of funerary furniture which included bronzes inscribed with the boastful achievements of the great man, his weapons, and his many personal belongings. The body of the nobleman was lavishly adorned with jade jewelry and other ornamentation and, as with so many early people, spattered or sprinkled with some form of red pigment, the same color being imparted to the hard-packed earth on which the coffin rested. Almost always dogs were buried with these important individuals, usually one below the tomb and one above, obviously to protect the body from the evils of the spirit world approaching from either direction.

In the tomb itself, surrounding the casket, were the bodies of the slaves and followers who shared the doubtful honor of accompanying the great personage into the shadowy world beyond the grave. With them was their armament—dagger-axes, bows and arrows, knives and other weapons with which to guard the noble one from harm. Sometimes a single huge grave was not sufficient and retainers and animal companions were buried in separate graves. There is a record of one chariot-and-horse burial at Hsiao-t'un in which four horses with their accompanying chariots and all their trappings along with beheaded retainers (presumably drivers) were all buried together and probably at the same time the master was buried in his more stately tomb nearby.

In the Hsiao-t'un area the excavations of Shih Chang-ju between 1933 and 1937 for the Academia Sinica revealed eleven different types of burials ranging from single prostrate individuals without burial gifts to collective burials with the beheaded bodies arranged in an orderly way in alternate directions. There were disorderly graves with a number of bodies having been buried helter-skelter and all beheaded, with their heads often piled in one group. There were burials where bodies were interred head downward, and one with a man kneeling and holding a dagger-ax in his right hand and a shield on his left arm. There were men buried with dogs, and graves of animals, including sheep, oxen and dogs, each grave containing a single species. But there were also graves containing mixed burials, dogs and sheep and oxen and sheep and even monkeys buried with pigs. Most of these were believed to be funerary gifts to someone buried close by and probably dedicated to them through prayers.

During the thirteenth excavation, in 1936, a burial was discovered in a pit underneath a Yin tomb which was of a surprising nature, and one that led to considerable speculation as the archeologists tried to interpret their findings. It was after the Shang-Yin tomb had been excavated that the explorers came upon the outline of a pit circular in form and quite large. The top of it is described as being about four feet below the ground level, and when emptied it proved to be eighteen feet deep. And to the amazement of the archeologists it contained literally thousands of oracle bones and turtle shells ranging from complete specimens to fragments of various sizes and shapes.

Considering the comparative scarcity of oracle bones and the value the archeologists placed on the discovery of sizable inscribed fragments, this find was so rich as to elate and amaze everyone. The enthusiasm of the excavators mounted as they worked through the top layer of ashy soil to reveal what turned out to be a large, sloping pile of oracle bones about a foot and a half deep at the top and about six and a half feet at the bottom.

The slope was from the north edge at the top to the south at the bottom and it was very obvious that these bones had been dumped in great loads. Some bones were even found on the top rim of the pit, indicating that they had been piled there during the process of dumping and had not been shoved

into the pit with the others. And there in the middle of the
pile of bones and turtle shells was the skeleton of a man on
his side in a flexed position with his chest, shoulders and
head protruding above the avalanche of bones that had obviously buried him.

The whole picture presented an amazing situation to Wang
Hsiang, who made the discovery, and to Tung Tso-pin, Hu
Fu-lin and their associates. It was obvious from the first that
the bones had not been placed in the pit in any orderly fashion. They lay in a very helter-skelter pile, face up, face down,
all sizes and shapes, some with inscriptions and some just
bare bones. There were turtle plastrons and carapaces, with
blackening and cinnabar rubbed into the characters etched
on them; and there were two inscribed turtle shells that had
been shaped like stone chopping knives, the first of their kind
the scientists had ever seen. The whole thing was really a
tremendous archeological haul and the scientists were jubi-
lant over it. Indeed, they extended their working period far
beyond the normal limits and well into a very hot and un-
comfortable summer in order to clean out the pit and assemble the material. They had more than three hundred
complete oracle bones and fragments enough to assemble several thousand more, which they proceeded to do, for the
inscriptions promised a revealing look back into the past of
the Shang-Yin City-State. But the mystery of the skeleton in
the pit was most baffling. Mr. Hu Fu-lin made some discerning observations and reached a very interesting if not pathetic
or grim conclusion.

In his report he explained that while it was a common oc-
currence to find fragments of oracle bones everywhere in the
diggings, some even imbedded in the pounded earth foundations of the buildings, on the whole they were rarely un-

earthed in great quantities. It is true that on two occasions pits had been found containing an orderly arrangement of oracle bones suggesting that they had been carefully filed away for safe keeping, or perhaps for future reference. They had also found a repository of some three hundred turtle shells, and on another occasion a number of scapulae with characters on them.

These had all been carefully placed in their respective pits, but in contrast, the mass of oracle bones that were unearthed in the pit under the Yin tomb had unquestionably been treated as so much refuse and cascaded into the open hole with little ceremony. They certainly could not be regarded as funerary furniture. As for the skeleton, its position was such that it seemed very unlikely the man could have been tossed into that pit on top of the bones, for he was actually partly buried in them. In fact, it looked for all the world as if he had jumped into the pit while the process of dumping the bones was taking place.

Could he have been the oracle priest whose duty it had been to read and interpret these bones? It apparently was not an unusual practice to bury a person with his equipment. Warriors were found buried with their chariots and horses, and in one instance an elephant handler was found buried with his elephants. Could this then be a similar case; the oracle priest being buried with his oracle bones, not as a human sacrifice, but as a matter of choice on his part; a point of honor since perhaps his oracular predictions had gone awry and the bones he used were being discarded as useless?

To support this conclusion Mr. Hu points out that a quick and early examination of the bones in the pit indicated that they all came from the same period, during the time of the very powerful and capable King Wu-ting. In conclusion, he decided that some great emergency may have made itself felt in the palace that necessitated throwing out all the oracle bones and causing the official in charge to commit suicide by being thus buried alive. Of course, it could be that Wu-ting was one king who didn't believe in oracle bones. Or perhaps he decided, as some kings did, that he was going to read and interpret his own oracle bones.

The speculations made possible by this strange find have ramifications which might shed light on later (600-500 B.C.) phenomena. Tung Tso-pin in one of his early articles on the names of oracle takers pointed out that some inscriptions were "signed" at the end by *shih-kuan*, "historians." In a large number of cases the name of the historian was identical with the name of the oracle taker. His conclusion was that actually the oracle taker, or diviner, was *also* the official historian of the king's court. If we keep the picture of the skeleton in its mound of records and Tung's identification of diviners with historians in mind, certain passages of *Tso's Commentary* (ca. 600 B.C.) take on the vivid colors of unvarnished truth. For in this remarkable history we read in a number of places that "The historian, rather than alter one line of his records under compulsion, committed suicide." Is this the meaning of the mute message left by a skeleton in a heap of turtle shells almost four thousand years ago?

But not all of the Shang-Yin burials took place in the great cemetery area, nor indeed did all of the human sacrifices have to do solely with deceased masters and their slaves and followers. Search trenches pushed out in several directions by Shih Chang-ju at Hsiao-t'un, while they did not uncover new tombs, did reveal the packed-earth floors and evidence of the foundation posts of the buildings, probably palaces, that had composed the beautiful capital of the Shang City-State. And

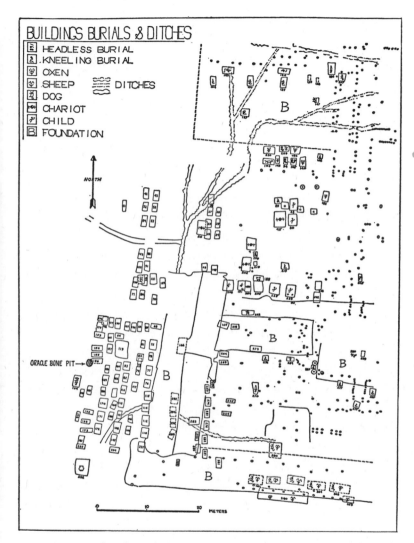

Map No. 3, showing various types of burials found at the site of the Shang City-State and their relation to the foundations of many of the structures they were supposed to protect definitely connected with these foundations and the structures built on them were burials of sacrificed human beings and animals, all intended to act as a defense against the evil spirits who were believed to demand propitiation after this grim fashion. (See Map 3.)

These purely sacrificial burials were found outside the foundations, as well as underneath and even on top of the foundations within the walls of the building they were meant to protect. Unquestionably, the executions and burials were accompanied by impressive ritual ceremonies and they were carried out only after careful divination by means of oracle bones. Indeed, the deep and abiding superstitions of the Shang-Yin people are reflected in the interpretations of the fragmentary text of many of these oracle bones, which indicate that the spirits of departed ancestors as well as the spirits of the River and the Earth all demanded sacrifices of both men and animals. They were rapacious creations of Shang superstitions, too, because they often appeared to demand the execution of even groups of men and animals. There is oracle bone evidence that ten, twenty and even thirty men were killed to suit these occasions, along with groups of oxen, sheep and dogs. And in some instances there is also reference to burnt offerings!

Apparently almost always a dog was buried underneath the middle of the floor area, but in one place a pit was found that contained the skeletons of five dogs. Possibly the builders had reason to believe that this structure, for some unknown reason, might be haunted by more than the ordinary number of malcontents from the world beyond. In the case of the human sacrifices, the men were beheaded and the oracle text indicates that in spite of the cruelty of the custom, great respect, if not indeed reverence, was shown to the unfortunate ones.

It is not hard to believe that efforts were made to convince the victims that they were peculiarly fortunate in being selected to enter the spirit world under such auspicious circumstances. How well they were able to convince the immolated ones of the pleasure of this distinction is, of course, a question.

The orientation of the structures to which these sacrificial burials were related seems to have been involved in some way, for some types of burial were always laid out from north to south, while other types were laid out with an east to west axis. The burials outside the foundations of the large and more important structures, probably the palaces, were located in front of the structure and were not too numerous. They were generally of animals. However, the burials outside the foundations of the less important houses apparently adjacent to the main building were always in the rear of the building and were many. Here were found beheaded skeletons of human beings as well as skeletons of animals. The burials that were made in the actual foundation of walls of buildings were generally located on either side of the entrance. They were in square pits, and the skeletons showed the men to have been buried in a kneeling position. Some were armed with dagger-axes and shields, and some also had dogs for companions. In some pits there were indications that there had been less substantial burial gifts from their relatives, such as food and clothing, to take with them on the dark journey.

There were fewer burials underneath the foundations than there were in the foundations themselves, or in the front and rear of the foundation area, and these seemed to be only below floors that were laid out in an east-west direction. These were mostly animal burials, the preponderance being dogs, though in some instances skeletons of oxen and sheep were found.

There is no indication of anything more than a general meaning to be found behind these interesting foundation burials, even by consulting the oracle bone translations. Professor Loehr of the University of Michigan points out in his translation and comments on Shih Chang-ju's article of 1947 that there have always been superstitions and unusual rites connected with the different phases of the construction of a house in China, as well as in many other corners of the world. Professor Loehr says that even today, in some of the provinces, when a house is started by breaking ground for the foundation, a sacrifice is made to the planet Jupiter and a secret ceremony is performed on the site of the proposed house by the carpenters who use such objects as a wooden horse and a rooster in their rituals. There are other ceremonious goings-on as the structure progresses, which include a sacrifice to the last member of the family who has entered the spirit world and still other sacrifices to the spirits of the surrounding area; particularly those likely to bring the most ill luck to the family of the home owner.

Besides exploring the original site in and about the village of Hsiao-t'un, Shih Chang-ju located several other likely archeological treasure houses in that same general vicinity. They were all close to the river and Shih Chang-ju explored them to a gratifying extent during the eight expeditions he directed and about which he wrote so completely.

There were other discoveries made besides those having to do with the Shang City-State for, as we already know, there are several distinct cultural layers to be found in the digs around Anyang. No further evidence of the Yang-shao age, that is to say, the people who made painted pottery, was uncovered within the Shang City beyond the single sherd that was found at Hsiao-t'un very early in the exploration efforts there. But abundant evidence of the Lung-Shan, or Black Pottery People, was found in several different sections of the area. All were positioned in such stratigraphic relation to the Shang-Yin level as to indicate very clearly that these people had established their town at the big bend in the Huan River long before the Yin people started to build the City-State of Shang there. Indeed, it is even possible that they were established in that strategic location on the peninsula when the invaders swept down upon them with their war chariots and, conquering them, made them slaves. It could be that the retainers who were so generously sacrificed with each royal funeral might have been those of the Black Pottery People who remained in servitude after their subjugation.

Artifacts of these Neolithic people were very numerous in some of the sectors. They included fragments of a variety of vessels of recognized types. Their coloring and decoration and marked thinness as well as the suggested shapes indicate very clearly that these people had developed the art of pottery making to an amazing degree of artistry. As at Ch'eng-tzu-yai, it was evident that they knew the processes of kneading, scraping and burnishing, and there was abundant evidence that they knew and used the potter's wheel in shaping their vases and various other vessels.

They used the bow, of course, and a variety of bone and stone arrowheads with round stems and triangular points were found, all of excellent workmanship and some of them well polished. Shell knives and shell saws resembling the same types of instruments used by the Shang-Yin people later were also found along with bone awls and stone axes of various shapes.

These people made their homes in the ground, too, for numerous dwelling pits were exposed, some large and some small. But, strangely enough, there did not appear to be any storage pits revealed in the exploration and what dwelling pits were opened up were shallow and small compared with Shang-Yin dwelling pits of a later period. These smaller pits contained an unrecognized light gray earth that suggested these people perhaps used a different type of fuel than the Shangs.

It is interesting to know that in the stratum above the level of the Black Pottery People (which is to say, the early Shang City level) dwelling pits are very numerous indeed and well-defined. So, too, are storage pits and a third type of trench which has not been thoroughly explained but which has been characterized as a type of water ditch.* (See Map 3.)

These all belong to the Shang-Yin people and by so much present a perplexing problem. For it seems strange indeed, if not almost incredible, that people who had the ability and ingenuity to construct horse-drawn vehicles such as their chariots, who were craftsmen enough to work in bronze, and who were capable of building temples and palaces of wood and pounded earth of impressive dimensions, as indicated by some of the floor areas, would elect to live in these unattractive holes in the ground.

The dugouts exposed in the later exploration of the An-

* The possible use of these, however, remains an interesting focus for speculation. The white, powdery remains of wooden planks and stakes all along their length indicate that they were something the Shang people took pains with. They could not be irrigation ditches or drains, for there is no incline either away from or toward the river. The excavators' only suggestion was that these ditches, when filled with water, would give the builders an absolute water level with which to measure and make of uniform height the pounded-earth platforms of their great structures so that all of the buildings of that section of the city would have their foundations level with each other.

yang site had, to be sure, been disturbed in many instances by unscientific digging so that their original shape had been altered and all indications of the interior arrangement obliterated. Indeed, they all had, in fact, at some time, become refuse pits filled with fragments of bones, broken pottery, arrowheads, stone knives, spear points, stone axes, ashes, shells, shell ornaments, kitchen refuse and a strange collection of dicarded trash. Most were round and shallow, but some were oblong or decidedly irregular. Their walls had been beaten smooth and in some instances covered with a thin mud plaster. And some showed evidence of having had steps leading down into them.

The storage pits were much deeper, and some of them were even larger in diameter than the dwelling pits, though most of them were smaller. Nearly all of them had become refuse pits, too, but there were some instances where the traces of the contents of the pit suggested that grain had been stored in them. In one the number and variety of objects found indicated that all the family treasure had been stored in it, literally thousands of separate articles.

Although it is true that there are many sections of China, particularly in the loess country, where there are entire villages in which the people live in pits dug out of the earth, it still is hard for the scientists to be convinced that the pits found at Anyang were the homes of the Shang-Yin people. It will be remembered that Andersson suggests that all of the pits were used for storage purposes in the fashion of present-day root cellars and that the people lived in houses that were much the same as the Chinese houses of today. Others agree with him to a greater or less degree. They believe that the slaves and the common people may have lived in the pit dwellings, while the nobility and the families of importance in the community lived in houses constructed on the pounded-earth platforms revealed by the excavators.

Although the City-State of Shang, which legend insists was a place of great magnificence, began to go to pieces and was ultimately deserted in 1026 B.C., there was abundant evidence in the eyes of the archeologists that the big bend in the Huan River was the site of many other settlements on a considerably lower scale. This is suggested by the fact that later generations of people buried their dead in a big graveyard that was uncovered and explored. And happily none of these later burials showed evidence of human sacrifice by way of pleasing the spirits of departed ancestors. One urn burial was found. It was the body of a boy, and two large urns were used as his coffin. The stratigraphy suggested that this unique burial took place slightly later than the last of the Shang people.

Quite a number of tombs of the Sui dynasty, A.D. 581-618, were revealed. They were mostly of pounded earth, though some of them were constructed of brick. All contained funerary furniture consisting of clay figurines, clay coins, dishes, bowls, iron mirrors and, interestingly enough, iron scissors. There were also tripods, vases and in some of the tombs were found pans with iron handles to hold charcoal.

There were also tombs of the T'ang dynasty, A.D. 713-841, and the funerary offerings were much the same as those found in the Sui tombs. A few Sung dynasty tombs, A.D. 960-1126, and two Ming dynasty tombs, 1368-1628, were also brought to light, both of them similar in shape and containing similar offerings. In the Ming tombs were found, among other things, coins dated as early as 1573 and as late as 1644.

There were more modern burials, the graves marked and protected by earthen mounds. Some of these were of the

Ch'ing dynasty and many, of course, were of the present. Indeed, one more mound grave was added by the exploring party when one of the men working in the excavation was killed.

Enter the　　　　10
Shang-Yin People

Whence came these Shangs? And when did they
drive out or capture the Black Pottery People, who lived on
the banks of the Huan River, and build their capital city at
the big bend near Anyang? Thanks to the indefatigable efforts
of the archeologists, both Chinese and western, who have
over the years spent many tiring hours at the Anyang site, a
reasonably satisfactory answer can be supplied to the second
question. But the answer to the first must still remain a mystery. No one knows where the Shangs came from. Legends
have it, however (and the archeologists more or less agree),
that in the early part of the second millennium before the
Christian era, which is to say somewhere between 1500 and
1300 B.C., a certain warrior king named P'an-keng suddenly
swept down upon the thriving village of Neolithic people on
the riverbank with his thundering war chariots and his horde
of bowmen and, storming the earthen wall that protected the
town, took possession of the dwelling site.

Similarly unreliable tradition has it this Shang king and

his princely offsprings raided and captured close to two thousand communities in northeast China, conquering all of them and establishing a dominion that extended from what is now western Shansi to Shantung and the shore of the Yellow Sea and southward into lower Honan. It is also said that these Shang kings had for one reason or another moved their capital city four or five times in as many centuries until they took possession of the site on the Huan River. There they proceeded to build the City-State of Shang from which to rule the surrounding country and the subjugated people, which they did for more than five hundred years. But where they came from or where their four or five previous capitals had been located is a mystery that has been completely baffling to the Sinologists until most recently when Cheng-chou, just south of the Yellow River, showed signs that it might have been one of the earlier capitals of the Shang-Yin people.

The Shang people were far from barbarians, tribes of which had long lingered on the flanks of the Late Stone Age communities on the fertile loess plains of the Yellow River basin, raiding and robbing whenever chance permitted. On the contrary, as we know, they brought with them an already well-developed culture rich in arts and crafts, and a well-established form of writing, containing several thousand words, which was the foundation of Chinese writing as it is today. They were formidable warriors, too, as revealed by a collection of stone, bone and bronze arrowheads and other weapons found at the foot of the remains of the pounded earth wall which once had protected the village of the Black Pottery People whom they probably conquered. The battles must have been long and furious before these people were finally subjugated and very likely made slaves.

This area in the bow of the big bend in the Huan River

must have been considered an ideal location for his capital by the conquering king. He unquestionably was influenced by oracular advice from the priests who were practicing divination by reading the cracks in the scapulae of oxen or the shells of turtles. Receiving ancestral approval, he moved in his people and their herds of domesticated creatures, and proceeded to build what must have been a very impressive city, judging from the archeological evidence that survived the rigors of time and climate.

It will be remembered that one area excavated contained pounded-earth foundations and other evidence of a number of buildings of remarkable size, some as long as one hundred twenty feet and as wide as thirty feet. There were others of varying size, the small ones being about ten by fifteen feet. This group showed careful planning and orientation, and is believed by some to have been the center of the Great City Shang. The largest structure was very probably the Yin Royal Palace and was surrounded by temples and the lesser buildings and courtyards that would grace an important capital of the Shang-Yin kings.

From the formation of these foundations and other evidence, not the least of which were the characters etched on some of the oracle bones, it is believed that we have a fairly clear idea of the simple architecture of these structures. They were probably long, single-storied buildings with gabled ends much like the majority of Chinese buildings today. But judging from the rare ornamental sculptures in marble, the impressions of wood carving and inlaid work, bronzes, and traces of paintings found in some of the royal tombs, there existed abundant facilities for decorating these royal structures. We can be sure they were ornate and beautiful palaces in sharp contrast with the scattered collection of earthen dugouts in which the common people and the slaves are believed to have lived. Lack of any trace of that durable object, the roofing tile, probably means the palace roofs were thatched or made of bamboo.

That there were accomplished artists and trained artisans in numbers in the Shang-Yin City-State cannot be doubted, either. From the archeological material that was gathered and the areas of the city site from which it was gleaned it has been suggested that there existed what may have amounted to guilds of craftsmen, each with its own district in the city. There have been found sections in which groups of potters, sculptors, workers in bronze and similar crafts unquestionably carried on their activities, for slag and other waste materials have been discovered in abundance in each of these areas.

That they possessed cloth of very fine weave, probably silk, is revealed by impressions on the earthen floor or a few tombs. The fabric itself had long since disappeared, but its texture was clearly imprinted in the pounded earth which filled the tombs. They wove baskets, made huge earthen urns and had shell, bone and marble buttons—some so small and delicate that they could only have been used on silk. They had beautifully carved jade ornaments and jade and shell combs and hairpins, worn by men and women alike. Chime stones and the *hsüan* or Chinese ocarina indicate that they had developed music to an unexpected degree, and oracle bones tell us that they possessed drums, which were used in war as well as for entertainment.

Knowing all these facts and many more as a result of the diligence of the archeologists, it is not hard for us to conjure up an exciting picture of the Great City Shang on any bright sunny day when it was the center of government for outlying communities. We can easily imagine its narrow, unpaved streets teeming with a heterogeneous humanity: begrimed bronze founders, sweating laborers, colorfully clothed and wispy-bearded elder citizens, street hawkers, beggars, vendors of parrots and monkeys, bone and leather armored bowmen, soldiers with bronze helmets (perhaps even bronze face masks), their voices a cacophony of excitement.

It is not hard either to imagine, sounding above all this, the imperious shouts of approaching outriders or the beating of warning drums as the clatter of horses' hooves and the rattle of chariot wheels announce the dashing approach of some noblemen hurrying importantly toward the royal palace, scattering the crowd in all directions. Or the more quiet and orderly approach of a retinue of slaves carrying the colorful palanquin of some nobleman's wife, on her way to return an important visit, disdainful of the crowd of commoners who press back against the walls to allow her room enough to pass in the narrow street while they ogle her curiously.

Here then are the beginnings of the true Chinese civilization as far back as it can be traced. Yet it is all too evident that this is indeed far from the start of the culture that is so well developed when the Shang-Yin people are first encountered in their city-state on the banks of the Huan River. It must have taken many centuries for them to move up out of the darkness of the Paleolithic Age to the beginning of the Bronze Age. But where they accomplished all this and where they appeared from so suddenly is still a lively debate.

Many scholars contended for a long time (and some still do) that the Shang-Yin people were originally nomads who followed their herds from one grazing ground to another until they found the North China Plain, where they settled down and developed their culture. Others, however, insist that they were essentially tillers of the soil rather than herdsmen. They insist that as farmers they were mostly interested in their crops, the amount of rainfall to be expected, and other factors that are important to an agricultural people. This is reflected in the many inscriptions that have been worked out by scholars who are expert in reading the oracle bones from the Anyang site. It is true, of course, that they had domestic animals, notably the dog, the horse, goats, oxen, sheep, water buffalo, pigs and numerous other creatures, for bones of about twenty different species were found and identified by the excavators at Anyang and by the Cenozoic Laboratory. Indeed, even the bones of elephants were unearth and recognized. But since elephants are not natives of China, or at least that section of it, the conclusions are that they had been brought in from some other part of Asia and trained to handle big, heavy timbers used in building some of the city's largest structures.

There are very few references to pastoral activities in the inscriptions on the oracle bones, and when flocks of domestic animals are mentioned, there is often an implication that they were being reared for sacrificial purposes. There are, to be sure, some inscriptions reporting the encroachment on Shang pasture lands by herdsmen from neighboring kingdoms, and it is even possible that this was sufficient reason to fight a war, for there is mention of this, too, on some of the oracle bones.

But the preoccupation of both kings and the commoners was with weather, crops, supplications for rain, and all the other interests that would be primary in the minds of people who cultivate cereals. As a matter of fact, weather was of such great importance to the Shang people that the king and his ancestors were in a measure held responsible for it. At a later time we know a king's success and popularity depended on the accuracy of weather prognostications to a very great degree and he, to protect himself, doubtless gathered about him the best weather prophets he could find. It may be assumed their jobs were not carefree occupations, however, for too many bad predictions probably meant that heads would roll.

The most important crop of these agricultural people seems to have been millet, though wheat is referred to very frequently in the oracle bone inscriptions. Rice is also mentioned, though there is not much evidence of the type of irrigation necessary for a good rice crop, and Anyang is considered too far north for growing rice at the present time. There is a kind of high-ground rice, and also a wild rice that may have figured in Shang economy. It is known that they also grew a type of clothing fiber very much like hemp, and it is presumed that they probably grew other plants, the fibers of which were used for weaving cloth. There is also reference made to silkworm cocoons, and the assumption is they were well advanced in the development of silk fabrics.

Undoubtedly the Shang farmers grew many other food plants not mentioned by the oracle bone inscriptions, all evidence of which has been erased by time. However, it is known that they, and particularly the noblemen, were great huntsmen, for there are numerous references to the game killed by various hunting parties. The inscribed bones reveal that organized hunts were carried on in which dogs and probably beaters were used to drive the game toward waiting bowmen. And there was a wide variety of game to be had on the plains and in the nearby mountains, for references to wild creatures bagged on some of these hunts range from deer and wild boars to badgers and rabbits. These hunts were tremendous slaughters, too, for apparently it was not uncommon for the huntsmen to bring back creatures of all kinds, numbering in the hundreds, and all this no doubt was celebrated by lusty feasting and commemorated by grateful sacrifice to the spirits of benevolent ancestors.

It is interesting to observe here that as the Shang-Yin people have given us the beginning of Chinese writing, so too have they furnished us with the first evidence of Chinese ancestor worship which has come down through the years, and even today, we are told, plays an important part in the personal religion of the Chinese people, communism notwithstanding. And like the writing of the Shangs, so too is the cult of ancestor worship seen to be so fully developed as to suggest a history that must have extended back into the past for many centuries.

The Chinese have always venerated their elders, but when these aged ones passed on into the spirit world they then acquired immeasurable power for good or evil. Thus, by so much, it was considered more important to seek their advice and blessing on any project than it had been when they were still alive and consulted because of their wisdom and experience. There was a certain superstitious necessity about this communing with the dead, for it was well known that ancestral spirits expected to be consulted and if they were not, they were easily offended. If this happened, woe betide the project contemplated and the earthly descendants interested in it, for the spirits were very jealous and quick to anger.

Beyond this fear of incurring spirit wrath, however, there was also the motivation of love and veneration. Indeed, many sacrifices were unquestionably made on the part of mortals by way of demonstrating their affection for the departed ones. This is proved by costly gifts buried with the deceased, probably far more expensive than could readily be afforded by the family. And it is a well-known fact that the food set out for the spirits' consumption was far better than that placed on the family table. Some of the game from any hunt, possibly the choicest, was used for sacrificial offerings to the ancestral gods whom men tried to impress with their gratitude. Inscriptions on the oracle bones often mention that one nobleman or another went hunting for the very special purpose of securing game to be used as a sacrifice.

But while food constituted most of the sacrifices, other things were used. Sacrifices ran the gamut from the very simple meals placed beside the corpse of a recently deceased relative or on the grave after burial to pouring wine on the ground, killing and offering the bodies of all types of domestic animals, rare ornaments, shell money, bronzes and even the gruesome offering of human sacrifices: children, slaves, servants, wives, and in the case of important noblemen, their ministers and their soldier bodyguards.

Much of the sacrificing was done as part of the funeral rites for the deceased one, but besides the spirits of departed ancestors, the Shang people had other gods to worship and sacrifice to for various reasons. There were omnipotent daemons in the earth, in the wind, in the river, and the four quarters of the heavens. Also there were a variety of dragons who must be kept happy. They are mentioned in the inscriptions on the oracle bones. So are a number of other deities, the most important by far, the great god Ti, though no one has found any clear explanation of who or what he was.

Who originated the interesting idea of communicating with the spirit world and importuning these gods and ancestral spirits for advice through the medium of tortoise shell or scapulae divination is another of the many archeological mysteries of China that remain buried in the void of the past.

As we are already aware, the Black Pottery People of Ch'eng-tzu-yai practiced scapulimancy to a certain degree. This was revealed by the ox and deer scapulae that were found in the digs at Lung-shan. Many bore evidence of having been used for divination purposes. But did these people originate the practice or did priests or oracles of a much earlier period invent this method of communicating with their special deities? No one knows the answer, but it is obvious that the Black Pottery People, unlike the men of the Painted Pottery culture, had this in common with the Shangs.

Certain it is, however, that the Shang-Yin people, whether they adopted the idea from the Black Pottery People or whether they developed it quite independently of outside influence, conceived a very much improved method of divination. They also, thereby, unintentionally contributed a great deal to our knowledge of the Shang City-State and Chinese history as we know it today.

The oracles of the Ch'eng-tzu-yai people did not make a record of the subjects on which the advice of the gods was sought, or at least they did not inscribe such records on the divination bones. But the Shang-Yin people did, and in many instances, as we know, the inscriptions were revealing in a number of significant ways. Scholars, by studying them, have been able to learn, for one thing, the variety of concerns most important to the Shang people. Inscriptions run from crops, weather and war to good luck or bad luck in any type of venture, questions of sickness or good health, fortunes in hunting, battles, journeys, sacrifices and announcements to be made to the gods they are importuning.

Dreams were very often interpreted, too. In fact, these inscriptions cover all subjects which might cause the average human being some worry, particularly if he felt that by not asking for higher advice he might bring down the wrath of spirits and suffer the results. Through these inscriptions scholars have been able to sketch a good picture of the higher levels of community life during the Shang-Yin era. They have been able to establish the names of a succession of rulers and the periods of their reigns; they have also learned much of the technique of divination by means of oracle bones, which by itself is a highly interesting subject.

Unquestionably there was a temple where a particular group of priests carried on these divinations, beginning with the preparation of bones or tortoise shells and ending with the recording of success or failure of the oracular pronouncement. According to Professor H. G. Creel in *The Birth of China,* one collection of bones was found at Anyang so neatly arranged as to suggest that the priests had filed away their divinations for a whole year. Was it to check results at the end of the year, or to show the ruler exactly what he had wanted presented to the gods in case he ever asked? It would be interesting to know.

Some believe that the tortoise shell was the most potent medium through which to approach the gods for advice and direction. The tortoise has always had an interesting place in Chinese mythology, and the special type of tortoise most used in divination was one then found in the area of Anyang. It is known to biologists as *Pseudocadia Anyangensis* and a University of Michigan zoologist has dryly suggested that the creature could not bear the heavy responsibility of this oracular correspondence, for it is now extinct.

It was the plastron, or belly shell, of the turtle that was most used by the priests, after the animal was consecrated to the ancestral deities. First the shells were scaled and highly polished, and then, doubtless with considerable ceremony, prepared for use by having numerous oval depressions bored into them. The number depended upon the size of the shell and, of course, the number of times it was to be used for divination purposes.

When the help or advice of their ancestral gods was desired, priests and suppliants presumedly gathered in the temple. Then with proper ceremony the questions were asked and sometimes cut or carved on the shell. Then the priest by applying an intensely heated stylus of some sort to the depression to be used or possibly by just dropping a red-hot wood coal into the depression, watched for cracks to appear in the shell about the pit that was used. Generally two cracks formed, one running lengthwise along the axis of the oval pit and the other laterally from the center or thinnest part of the depression outward, generally forming the shape of a broken H, like this:

or this:

It was by interpreting these cracks in their own special way that the priests answered the queries about which information was being sought. To indicate what a lasting effect this divination process had on Chinese civilization, it should be noted that

(pronounced *pu*)

is still the Chinese character for "fortune telling."

In using bone from the shoulder blade of an ox or from a section of a leg bone, careful preparations were made, as they were with the turtle shell. They were polished and pitted, but it is not known whether the creature, like the turtle, was always sacrificed first. In the case of the leg bone, it was split in such a fashion that a smooth, flat, fairly thin section could be secured. It was formerly suggested that, possibly because of the scarcity of the tortoise, the shells of these creatures were reserved for the use of especially important people or important occasions. We now know that animal bones, including human skulls, were used earlier, and turtle shells were a later introduction. It is known, too, that often when the king went on a journey somewhere a tortoise shell was taken along so he could handily seek the advice of gods at any point and change his plans if things did not look propitious.

It is possible that the Shang-Yin rulers gradually reached a point where they were dependent upon the advice of priests who read these oracles. It appears that some of the kings were circumscribed in their actions by their belief in the directions they got from the spirits and they sought information at the beginning of every ten-day period, which constituted a Shang week. If it appeared that they might be entering a period when the portents were all wrong, they put off making any grave decisions until the signs were more favorable.

All this, of course, placed tremendous power in the hands of the priests, and there can be little doubt that many of them made the most of it. They would be scarcely human if they did not. Most certainly many of them vicariously shaped the policies of the Shang City-State. There is a curious twist to this, though. Wu-ting, the great-grandson of P'an-keng, supposed founder of the City Shang, is traditionally known as a virtuous and powerful king. His oracles are noted for the fact that they contain a good many warnings of ill tidings and predictions of outcome which seem to be contrary to the king's desires. On the other hand, Wu-ting's successors, Ti-yi and Ti-hsin, who were nearer in time to the final downfall of the City Shang, have only favorable predictions from their oracles. From this it would appear that later kings had diviners who were sycophantic rather than diligent, and the gloomier predictions which Wu-ting was given kept both the king and the priests on their toes.

War, then as in any other age, was of deepest concern to the kings and their subjects, and a number of the inscribed oracle bones have to do with that subject, suggesting that the Shangs were a warlike people. They must have been if, as one historian records it, they conquered more than eighteen hundred communities—an amazing number. Just how much the oracle priests were responsible for promoting these conquests cannot be known, of course, but certainly they had many opportunities to sway the thinking and intentions of the Shang rulers, for one can be very sure an attack was never launched without first asking the spirits whether the time was right and the attack would be successful. There are numerous inscriptions in which the Shang ancestral gods are asked whether they favor such and such an attack and whether, if it were undertaken, these same gods would lend their assistance.

The bone inscriptions and, of course, the extensive excavations at Anyang reveal that the Shangs were well equipped for welfare. They possessed the powerful composite reflex bow constructed of laminated wood, bone, and sinew. This bow has long been considered the most powerful ever developed, beside which the vaunted English longbow was almost a feeble weapon. Whereas the average war or hunting bow has a draw of from seventy up to a hundred pounds, some of these reflex bows had a pull well above a hundred and seventy pounds. Indeed, some were so powerful it is said they could only be used by having the archers lie on their backs and brace the bow with their feet while they used both hands to pull the string back and release an extra long arrow. This was a siege bow which could shoot arrows over a protecting wall four or five hundred yards distant. Whether the Shangs possessed any weapons of that type we do not know, but inscriptions reveal that they were skilled archers.

They made other weapons, including the lance and the bronze dagger-ax—the most typically Chinese weapon. And they had one type, if not indeed several types of armor. In one of the royal tombs opened during the excavation at Anyang, a collection of bronze helmets numbering more than seventy was found. It is believed that armor of leather and wood or leather and bone was also used by Shang fighting men, but almost all traces of equipment of this type have succumbed to the destructive dampness in the yellow earth.

That the great war chariot was an important part of the armament of the Shang nobility has been very well established by the bone inscriptions. These were two- and sometimes four-horse vehicles, which besides carrying the commander and his driver also often carried spearsmen armed with long bronze-headed lances, or archers, or conceivably one of each as bodyguards to the commander. It is believed that sometimes these chariots were used in mass formation as the armies of the west used cavalry. But, of course, such chariot charges could be more easily stopped than cavalry, nor were they of any use against a walled city unless and until the walls had been breached and there were no moats or ditches to interfere. It is known that the noblemen who commanded the fighting forces went into the field in their own chariots, from which battle flags were flown and from which commands were thundered to the troops on huge, resounding war drums.

The oracle bone inscriptions also indicate the size of some of the armies put into the field by the Shangs. A force of a thousand to twelve hundred men seemed to be about average, though frequent reference is made to forces of three thousand and even five thousand men. All this suggests that some of the campaigns organized and carried out were very impressive conflicts. To be sure that they were well planned and would be successful, the interest and cooperation of dwellers in the spirit world were always thoroughly canvassed before they were launched.

The Shang kings, as we know, had many vassal states from which they drew support when they felt they could trust the enfiefed dukes or lesser noblemen. Concern about whom they could trust is reflected in inscriptions on the oracle bones. There are many of them that query the spirits whether certain allies can be depended upon to furnish reliable reinforcements if needed. Other inscriptions concern warnings received from outlying towns of roving enemy bands, night attacks, and raids on the domains of some supposed friendly nobleman. And the question is often asked whether the Shangs should send assistance. So evidently Shang loyalty depended on the voice of the gods or the intelligence of the priests. The latter and the ancestral deities they served apparently guessed right more often than not. For a period of almost five centuries the Shangs were able to beat back their enemies and maintain what later became a slowly disintegrating empire until the Chou people overwhelmed them to become their conquerors.

Bronzes 11
and Weapon Sets

The fact that the bare, lumpy mountains which subside into the plain some fifteen miles northwest of the Shang City site contain no usable copper and tin deposits is only one of the minor mysteries which occupy the minds of archeologists in China. Nowadays people speak of the "Bronze Age" in much the same way as they speak of any other period of time and forget the impact which the discovery and utilization of that alloy of copper and tin had upon the men who lived then. The more thoughtful are aware that bronze had more potentialities than copper; because of its superior hardness and workability, it was immediately put to use in weapons, chariot fittings and armor, but few of us think of how this brilliant golden alloy must have appealed to the eyes of its first users and how imposing that beauty must have been in that age.

Of all the objects cast during the Bronze Age which have so far come to light, none is so impressive as the great ritual vessels cast in the hearths of the Shang State. The skills lavished on these beautiful vessels, the inscriptions upon them, the fact that they were cherished by the living and were fit for the most noble dead; all these indicate quite clearly that what we appreciate today as objects of great esthetic value were also venerated in their own day for their beauty and their symbolism.

There is a legend, so persistent that it must have a foundation of fact, that there were nine great bronze vessels which were the symbols of sovereignty the Chou kings took over when they defeated the Shang some eleven hundred years before the birth of Christ. The tradition has it that these Nine Brazen Cauldrons continued for five hundred years to be the visible sign of kingship, and the eye of every petty prince was fastened on them. As the power of the Chou dynasty weakened, other states in China made attempts to get these fabled bronzes. Once they were promised to the country of Ch'i if Ch'i would come to Chou's rescue. When the war was over and the Chou king had to pay off with the Brazen Cauldrons, he began to regret his promises and sought ways to get out of giving up the valued urns.

"Great sovereign, I beg you to rest easy," said Yen Shuai, his advisor, "and allow your servant to go eastward to Ch'i and speak to their king."

When Yen Shuai arrived in the capital of Ch'i, he said:

"Chou trusted in the rectitude of your great country. Father and son, minister and prince have been sustained and it is our wish that the Cauldrons be given you. It remains only to know by what road they will be fetched to Ch'i."

"We shall ask right-of-way from Liang."

"You must not, my lord; Ch'u's sovereign and ministers have long coveted the Cauldrons and plotted for them in the courts of Shè. Once the bronzes enter Ch'u they will not leave."

"But, by what route then may we fetch the bronzes to Ch'i?" asked the king.

"This is just what has concerned my humble prince," replied Yen Shuai, "for the Cauldrons are not so many vinegar jugs or sauce pots to be carried to Ch'i dangling from the hand or clutched at the breast. Nor can they be hustled off to Ch'i like hare-started horses or bird-harried crows. Of old when Chou conquered Shang and got the Cauldrons, ninety thousand men drew a single bronze and nine required one hundred and eighty thousand men with troops and their officers, tackle and gear all readied to accomplish the task. Now, though your majesty has the men for it, what troubles your servant is the route by which they may be brought out."

"It has seemed these several times, sir, that you do not intend to present them at all," said the king.

"I would not dare deceive your mighty state," replied Yen Shuai. "Let the king merely say outright by what route they are to come forth and my humble prince will move the Cauldrons at your command." But the king of Ch'i ceased his requests.

This story, translated from the *Chan-kuo Ts'e,* a work which may be as early as the third century B.C., is obviously fictional but it serves to indicate that Shang bronzes were as esteemed in the past as they are admired today. Nearly every great museum in the world has some of these vessels; they are prized for their graceful or powerful shapes, for the composition of their high-relief décor and for the variety and beauty of their patinas, ranging from a lovely waxy, malachite green through blue-green and occasionally soft reds. The colors depend on the composition of the metal to some extent, but mostly on the minerals of the soil which covered them for thousands of years.

There are in existence now scores of vessels which bear the hallmarks of bronzemasters who were certainly men of the Shang state—that these, as well as thousands of pieces of chariot fittings, weapons and the like, should have had their origins in an area which today has no usable copper and tin deposits (Chinese bronzes did not contain lead) is, as mentioned, a minor mystery. Fortunately, China has always been occupied by people who spoke the same language that is spoken today, and local tradition remains strong enough to yield half the answer to the mystery. The mountains nearest the site of the ancient capital are called T'ung-shan (copper mountains) and a tiny village with its cotton and wheat fields is still known as Nan T'ung-yeh (copper-foundry South). Probably the metal used to be mined in these mountains.

But if the solution to the minor mystery is relatively simple, the answers to the major puzzle—where and when did the marvelous complex of exquisite bronze technique with its stylized and naturalistic decoration begin?—are still far off. Nor can they hope to be found except by uncovering hundreds of Bronze Age sites to gain more knowledge of the relatively less advanced periods of bronze working in China. As the situation now stands there seem to be the strongest possible reasons for relating the curved, ring-handled Shang knives with southwestern Siberia in the area around the sources of the Ob and Yenesei rivers. Perhaps the exuberant "zoomorphic" (animal-form) decorations which peer out at the beholder from almost every bronze object associated with Shang are in some way related to the steppe nomads, too. But the trouble begins when one takes a stand on the question of the direction in which the bronze working and design flowed.

As with Painted Pottery, the question is: Did it originate in China and spread from there, or the reverse? Part of the difficulty is a sense of abrupt explosion in decorative patterns found on ritual bronzes of the Shang and early Chou periods. William Willets in his two-volume work, *Chinese Art,* suggests that one of the great mysteries in Chinese archeology still to be solved is the reason behind what he calls the sudden and spontaneous outburst of animal representation and the way it coincides with the first historical dynasty and the Bronze Age in China. He feels that some of the bronze figures have never been equaled anywhere else for their verve and vitality.

Figure 1

On ritual bronzes the animal patterns are often divided into three bands around the outside of the vessel. In Figure 1, two sets of jaunty little animals march toward each other, separated by the face of an animal looking outward. But on careful observation the four high-stepping creatures suddenly lose their outflung forelegs (there seems to be a ball under each) and this foreleg will unexpectedly change into the lower jaw of a gap-mouthed beast which is standing still. The central band of high-relief decoration is often the composite animal face known as *T'ao-t'ieh* or "glutton mask," so-called, it is said, because the lower jaw is not even visible.

The symbolism of this is still obscure, but the artistic possibilities for the Shang designer were enormous. On many

Figure 2

bronzes there is rather clearly a face with hornlike ears (or earlike horns), eyes and muzzle well defined, and a smaller twin of the face placed right in the middle of its forehead (Figure 2). But notice how this same pattern can be worked also to look like two horned and beaked creatures squared off at each other (Figure 3). Or, if looked at long enough, two

Figure 3

ridiculous long-nosed creatures seem to be running away from each other. Throughout the background are the square-cornered spirals which the Chinese archeologist and bronze collector calls *lei-wen* (thunder pattern). The reason for this term is unclear as is also so much about the origin, development and ritual use of these handsome bronze vessels.

The handles on several types of bronze vessels are generally worked in the form of beasts and birds, some stylized and some quite pictorial, but all done with a great deal of spirit. Other vessels had lids with single handles on top for lifting them off. These, too, are often in the form of birds. When ring handles are attached to the bronzes—this happens most often with vessels which are probably Chou period productions—they are designed to appear held in the mouth of an animal. In the vessels of high, slender proportions and also on the rather long legs of several classes of bronze, there appears a dagger-shaped design which Chinese antiquaries

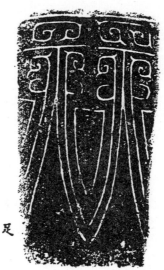

足

Figure 4

called *ch'ui-hua* (drooping petals). Western art historians call it the cicada shape, which it may have once represented (Figure 4).

Whatever it may have been to the Shang designer at first is relatively unimportant, for when it was elaborated, there appear within it serpentine creatures and other animal forms.

When all of these features of Shang and early Chou design are coupled with the fact that some bronzes are entirely shaped in images of birds and elephants, it is perfectly clear that this tradition of animal design is fully developed when we first find China in the Bronze Age. It is equally obvious that Shang bronze décor is the end product of a long development, but neither the Painted Pottery (with one small, but important exception) nor the Black Pottery of Neolithic China shows any trace of this decorative tradition.

The same is not true of the *shapes* of the bronze vessels, however. The bulging, hollow-legged earthenware pots (a wonderfully efficient design) were unquestionably the ancestors of the hollow-legged Shang bronze forms. Certain pitcher shapes in pottery were probably the inspiration for one of the most striking shapes among bronzes: the high-legged *chüeh* with the curious upright pommel-shaped handle or handles on its upper rim and the sweeping flare of its spout.

One fact about the Shang bronzes is agreed upon by all who know them—they are priceless. But when a price is set upon a good specimen in first-class condition, it may range from two to ten thousand dollars. The story is told that several wealthy Chinese families in the late nineteen-thirties began to fear the rapid inflation of their currency and invested their savings in Shang and Chou bronzes. After the end of the Second World War, they recouped their fortunes handsomely by the sale of these antiques which had been carefully hidden for a decade.

More important, however, is the painstaking study of them by archeologists and art historians which has revealed so much about the technological and intellectual accomplishments of the Shang people. By taking into account all the evidence, some archeologists feel that the method by which the bronze vessels were cast was the *cire-perdue,* or "lost-wax" process. If this is how he did it, then the first step the bronzemaster must have taken was to prepare a core model—complete with legs in many cases—from good plastic clay which would hold its shape well when dry. The outside layer of the core contained fire-clay or powdered fire-brick, for it had to stand up to the shock of molten bronze. Upon this core would then have been brushed layers and layers of wax which would be as thick as the wall of the vessel was to be.

This wax model was next carved, tooled and worked into exactly the designs which would later become those seen on the outside of the vessel's surface. If there was to be an inscription on the outside of the bronze's surface, it was built up in wax, not incised, for most characters on bronzes are seen in relievo rather than intaglio. It would seem that the bronzemaster might also have been one of the very few people who were literate at that time.

The next step was most important. The bronzemaster's assistant would have been mixing a fine-ground watery clay with a binder and more of the powdered fire-brick. This was of the finest and most regular consistency, for it had to be brushed carefully over the entire wax surface, reaching every tiny crevice and covering every high-relief ornamentation. If these first layers failed to penetrate everywhere, there would be flaws on the surface of the vessel.

The later coats could be coarser and could be brushed on less meticulously—perhaps applied by the assistant instead of the bronzemaster—until a sufficiently strong outside shell then buttressed the wax design. There would be waxen plugs running from the wax design through the outer clay shell so that the melted wax could drain off to have its form taken by the molten bronze. Pins of some sort must have run through the outside shell of clay, through the wax image and into the inside core to keep the latter from settling when the wax was melted out and the bronze was still in a liquid state. These pins were cunningly placed so that the holes they left could be closed later in a manner so skillful as to defy detection.

Some bronzes were cast from sectional molds, pieces of which were found in the early excavations near Hsiao-t'un, it will be remembered. The process with these is similarly complicated, but the molds can be used more than once, and the sectioning of them was cleverly concealed in the surface design of the vessels.

But if the Shang bronzes presented many mysteries to the archeologists, so too did Shang arms. Despite the fact that Chinese Bronze Age weapons held the entire loess area for a thousand years before the Christian era in the west, there was almost nothing known concerning the shapes and uses of these arms until the last thirty years. Even then there were few except museum personnel who were acquainted with the peculiarities of these ancient weapons. In the last decade, however, a great deal of information has been published: *Chinese Bronze Age Weapons,* by Professor Max Loehr appeared in 1956; *Chang-kuo Ping-ch'i shih K'ao* (A Draft History of Chinese Weapons) by Chou Wei was published in mainland China in 1957; and Bulletin No. 22, *Academia*

Sinica (T'aiwan), 1950, contains an important article by Dr. Li Chi and the careful and imaginative article of Professor Shih Chang-ju on the equipment of Shang soldiery.

Professor Shih had the responsibility of writing up the Anyang excavations which he did although he was a thousand miles removed from the site of the Shang capital on Formosa. In 1948, Academia Sinica had transported tons of material to Formosa from its former headquarters in Nanking. This included all the photographs taken at the Anyang site, along with the sketches and most of the actual articles that had been excavated in and around Hsiao-t'un, and the professor had all of this material available when he untertook his study of the equipment of the warriors of the Bronze Age.

He selected six burials which he felt should contain sets of the warriors' weapons, and proceeded to make a careful study of the contents of these graves. Among them were four chariot burials, one burial of a man and a horse, and one of a man alone. From the photographs and data which went with them Professor Shih made sketches of all the articles which seemed to be related to weaponry rather than some other aspect of the burial and then proceeded to do a remarkable piece of scholarly detection and reconstruction.

To begin with, he had to eliminate a number of bronze objects which were known to be chariot fittings or harness decorations. And there were also certain objects, such as a handsome polished stone dagger-ax blade and polished stone arrowheads which had to be set aside because they were obviously ritual funerary furnishing. But there were enough bronze objects left to allow the broadest possible scope for the professor's reasoning and imagination.

At first he was baffled by several things. For instance, the groups of arrowheads all lay in an orderly oval array, which

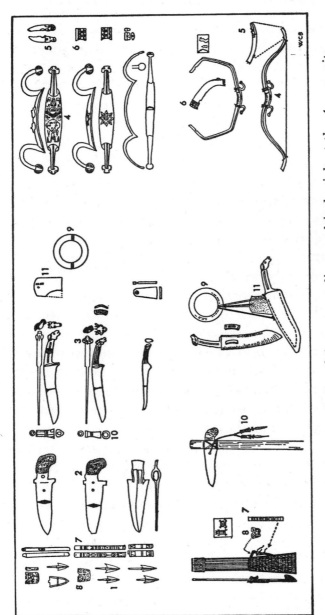

Shang-Yin weapons as reconstructed from parts discovered in burials at the Anyang site

made it evident that they had been tipped arrows in a quiver. The shafts of the arrows and, of course, the quiver itself, being made of wood or other perishable material, had long since disappeared. But the arrangement in which the bronze points lay corroded together suggested a quiver quite unlike any with which Professor Shih was familiar until, after a diligent search, he found a photograph in a Japanese publication of a very old wicker-rack quiver which had come from China originally.

He was able to see sufficient evidence of a woven wicker pattern impressed in the bronze of the arrowheads to indicate that a quiver of this type had probably been used. There were other somewhat baffling objects that required considerable study and deduction, not the least of which were certain "bow-shaped ornaments" in each grave. These have long been the object of much speculation and disagreement among Sinologists, some contending they were forms of harness decoration and others that they were grips for the powerful reflex bows that obviously must have been buried with these warriors. The material of which the bows were made, whether horn, bone or wood, had long since disintegrated, but in every grave the position of this "bow-shaped ornament" was such that Professor Shih decided it lay exactly where a bow grip would be positioned, midway between certain metal or polished stone objects that were evidently bow tips. So he decided that they were unquestionably ornamental bow grips.

All in all, Professor Shih did a remarkably thorough and painstaking piece of work analyzing and reconstructing the armament of the Shang warrior, even to working out the probable size and construction of his shield, only the vaguest traces of which were to be found in these graves.

The result of this remarkable study allows us to imagine a

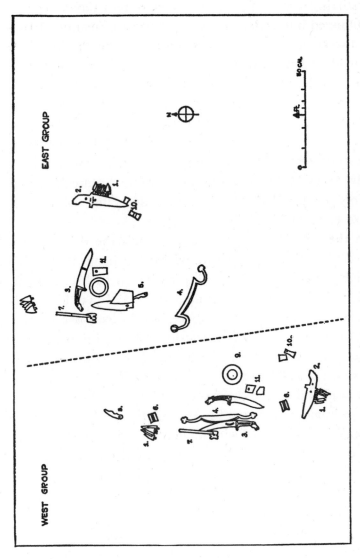

The arrangement of some of the components of the weapons as revealed in their original position when the graves were first opened

very stirring scene as this fighting man of four thousand years ago plunged into action. We can picture a formation of two-man two-horse chariots thundering across the Anyang plain in a wild onslaught, with a tower of dust boiling up behind them. The heavy wheels of each chariot turn on gleaming bronze hubs which protrude far beyond each wheel rim. The body of the chariot is armored with tough, tightly shrunken leather emblazoned with sinuous but colorful animal faces and forms, the uglier the better. These chariots are drawn by sturdy Asian horses which are hitched to bronze-decorated chariots' center shafts by harnesses decorated with small bronze plates and medallions.

On the left side of each chariot stands the driver, bare-headed, the reins wrapped around his left hand, while with his right he cracks his long whip thong on its bronze shaft. At his waist swings a horse-headed knife, and over his shoulder hangs a bow case. On the driver's right hand the warrior sways to the movement of the chariot. A heavy bronze casque-helmet (feather crest streaming from it) covers his head and most of his face. The brow of the helmet is decorated with a ram's head and on the cheek-pieces are great whorl patterns, perhaps inlaid with turquoise. His left hand grips his curved leather shield, decorated with highly colored patterns echoing those on the sides of the chariot. In his right hand he carries his dagger-ax (for use when the time has come for infighting), but he can put both shield and dagger-ax in a rack on the side of the chariot, unsling the powerful bow from its shoulder case and loose as many as fifty bronze-tipped bamboo arrows, each three feet long, which he can pluck from wicker quivers lashed inside the chariot. There is also a spear standing upright in its chariot socket, perhaps with a characteristic

Shang point—broad, with lateral blades and a diamond-shaped cross section.

This was a fearsome war machine, and it swept the China plains for hundreds of years. But ultimately it met its match in an enemy whose armament looked deceptively simple. The nomadic horsemen who invaded the Shang domain were equipped solely with a more compact version of the reflex bow, and on horseback they could ride rings around the war-chariot and slay both its horses and its occupants before they could alter course. Bands of these horsemen raided China successfully for decades before the Chinese abandoned his war-chariot and loose, flowing gown for trousers, tight-wristed sleeves and a smaller bow as well as a swift pony. For centuries after chariots were abandoned, however, the common term for a truly powerful nation was still *wan-ch'eng chih kuo*—"a kingdom of ten thousand chariots!"

The Communists   12
Dig

Archeology in Communist China has suffered
from the fact that since 1950 it has been primarily a salvage
operation. The various Provincial Cultural Committees and
indeed the Archeological Institute under the Ministry of
Science has always been at the beck and call of whatever large-
scale engineering project was bearing down on sites of possible archeological importance. This has produced an
enormous number of finds with little time and few properly
trained men to conduct the excavations themselves. Fewer
men still were capable of sitting down with the accumulated
facts patiently to work out the theories that fit them.

Two examples will suffice to demonstrate the situation. In
1952, at Loyang, in the precincts of the T'ai-shan Temple
near the East Gate, a very curious example of turtle plastron
prepared for omen-taking was discovered by a training class
in field archeology. This plastron was unique in the fact that
the pits cut into it to prepare it for the application of a heated
stick or coal were not chiseled and gouged as had been the

case at Anyang, but were cut so that the depressions which were to receive the heated object were perfectly square. The oracle bone was just half of a complete plastron and it had been prepared with nearly twenty square indentations from which divination could have been made. That a Shang-Yin type of oracle bone should have been found so far west along the Yellow River as Loyang was interesting in itself. No one was available in Loyang to speculate on this interesting discovery (with any hope of drawing conclusions), so the object was reported to the Archeological Institute at Peking.

That same autumn, one hundred miles east along the Yellow River, at Erh-li Kang in Cheng-chou, *a training class in field archeology* discovered the richest Shang-Yin site that has come to light since Anyang. Over three hundred seventy pieces of animal bone prepared for oracle taking and eleven pieces of turtle shell to be used for the same purpose were discovered in the rubbish pits of this site. Once again, the finds may have been placed in the Provincial Museum, but the reports were referred to Peking and to Dr. Ch'en Meng-chia, asking him to comment on their significance.

It might be objected that now, years later, the severe shortage of adequate scholarly personnel would certainly be alleviated, but it is doubted that this is true. Taking into account the habits of the central government of the People's Republic, "persuading" citizens to make donations of their time for public works, for "Hate America Campaigns," for "Criticism and Self-criticism" sessions, for indoctrination periods, for fly-catching, rat-killing and sparrow slaughtering, for countless rectifications of attitudes . . . there has probably been a constant turnover of "training classes in applied archeology" and very little training of scholars to keep up with their own finds.

Certainly an exception to this general criticism is Dr. Ch'en Meng-chia himself (the scholar to whom the oracle bone finds were eventually referred), who is an older scholar and a recognized expert in the field of oracle bone inscriptions. His monograph, *Yin-hsü Pu-tz'u Ts'ung-shu* (A General Description of Oracle Bone Inscriptions), published in the summer of 1957, is of first-rate importance and covers all the Shang-Yin finds which included oracle bones, inscribed or otherwise. It is significant to note, however, that even this excellent piece of work was actually in its semifinal form as early as 1949.

The general picture of Shang-Yin excavations in China after the year 1937, which was the last that was carried out by the Academia Sinica at Hsiao-t'un according to the record made by Dr. Ch'en Meng-chia, included what he indicated was a semiofficial excavation in an abandoned moat outside the compound wall of Ch'ilu University in Chinan, Shantung Province. It was successful and considered profitable even though only one piece of oracle bone without inscription was found. It had been prepared with pits for divination purposes. Besides this a number of arrowheads were found with eight bronzes as well as bronze chariot fittings. This dig was carried on in 1948.

Two years later, in 1950, the Communist government, having organized the Archeological Institute, undertook several digs in the general vicinity of Anyang. One was undertaken along the borders of a village known as Ssu-p'an Mo, not far from where digs had been carried on from 1935 to 1937 on the edge of Hsiao-t'un, which was close at hand. This dig was started along a canal that carries water to the farms in the vicinity of Anyang and the city moat. At the same time another dig was in progress in the village of Hua-yuan, which is described as being just across the road south of Hsiao-t'un. Information about these excavations is very meager in this country chiefly because copies of *K'ao-ku Hsueh-pao,* No. 5, in which the reports were published, are very rare here.

From Japanese archeological circles, however, comes word that a large tomb was found and opened across the river from Hsiao-t'un though there is little information about what was recovered. It is known that during these digs about fifteen complete oracle bones, partially readied for divination, were found, and fragments of a few turtle shells also came to light. Just a single piece of bone was inscribed and in such a way as to suggest that it was a bone on which some young priest had been practicing the art of etching characters.

That same year other digs were started well south of Anyang, where surface clues led the diggers to begin an extensive excavation at Liu-li Ko, which is at least forty-five miles from Anyang. Evidently a rather extensive Shang-Yin site was exposed in which some very dramatic finds were made, the most important feature of which was evidence of the burial of at least five chariots.

This dig is believed to have been a very successful operation. It was particularly rich in evidence of scapulimancy, for forty-two pieces of water buffalo scapula were found along with twenty pieces of bovine scapula, and one pig shoulder bone. While none of these bones had inscriptions on it, all had been prepared for divination and had evidently been used for that purpose. The pits were all drilled deep and not placed in an orderly arrangement. Indeed, as they were located, it would have been impossible to etch characters on any of them, for they were so crowded that there was no room for even the briefest inscription. All of them showed evidence of having had fire applied, some directly to the flames, while others had hot stones or coals dropped into the pits. In many ways these bones suggested a crude form of scapulimancy very much like that found at the original Black Pottery site at Ch'eng-tzu Yai instead of the finished work found at the Shang capital site at Hsiao-t'un. Professor Ch'en felt that these pitted animal bones and their rude handling were in sharp contrast to the carefully inscribed work of the oracles of the royal household on the sacrificially prepared turtle shells found at Hsiao-t'un. They represented the difference between the professional efforts of the trained oracle and the workaday practice of the soothsayers of the more remote districts.

The most interesting discovery in 1952 was the turtle shell with the curiously squared pits mentioned previously as being found at Loyang and the location of an extensive Shang-Yin site at Cheng-chou where, among other things, were found bones prepared for divination by the use of a metal drill. All the pits showed conical bottoms and, in fact, a bronze drill was found jammed into an incompleted hole and broken off.

The following year, 1953, two pieces of inscribed bone were found at Erh-li Kang, in Cheng-chou, and sent to Professor Ch'en in Peking. The first was a section of rib bone from a bovine creature, probably an ox. This had very uncertain, shallowly etched characters and also had all the appearance of being a practice piece by some neophyte. The first piece was sent to Peking in May, and in September the second piece arrived. It had only one character inscribed on it. The next year a third inscribed piece turned up, and when later the excavations were extended to the area known as the People's Park, quite a number of turtle shell pieces were found, all prepared for divination purposes but without inscriptions.

In 1953, what is believed by Professor Ch'en to be a later development in the preparation of oracle bone technique appeared in Shensi. These are comparable with the turtle shell with the squared pits that was found at Loyang and which Professor Ch'en believes to be in fact a residual tradition of oracle bone divination that carried over into the Chou period. In support of this it should be mentioned that there were many other Chou dynasty artifacts unearthed in this dig.

The trail of Shang-Yin excavations over which Professor Ch'en leads us ends in 1955. But one other rather long excavation was undertaken in 1957 in Cheng-chou, outside the South gate. Here, from July to December, the exploratory trenches found the same culture layer observed at Erh-li Kang, and still lower they found two other distinct layers which were unlike the lowest layer of Erh-li Kang. The interesting complication which occurs with these lower layers of Shang culture (for so the reporters identify it) is the strong similarity which pottery shapes in these lower layers show to Yang-shao pottery. This is the reverse of what has previously been remarked; that the Shang vessel shapes resembled Black Pottery rather than Yang-shao.

When these excavations were completed in the new and important Shang-Yin site at Cheng-chou, the large cotton factory north of Anyang (already in operation for some time when the first excavations were made at Anyang in 1929) was being expanded. Again a salvage operation was undertaken, this time on the north side of the river, near the outskirts of the village known as Ta Ssu-k'ung (see Map 2). The reader may have noticed that the north side of the Huan River has been proving itself for thirty years to be the place of the dead for the Great City Shang. The royal necropolis was on the north bank at Hou-chia Chuang; the "elephant tomb" was also on the north bank. In 1953, south of Ta Ssu-k'ung (see Map 2) on the north bank twelve Shang-Yin tombs were uncovered, and lastly the excavation which began in February 1958 and was finished in March, twenty days later, uncovered fifty-one Shang tombs.

Typical of the speed that characterizes excavations in China today, 45,600 square meters of surface had been "drilled and tested" for the existence of tombs, and more than sixty tombs had been located and excavated, their contents noted and numbered and the area tidied up in less than twenty days. The writers of the report declare that this efficiency was possible "because of the leadership of party members attached to the factory." This seems likely. Granted that any middle-aged group of Anyangites is liable to contain the most experienced tomb probers in the world, the haste implicit in locating, excavating, examining and cataloging an average of three tombs a day for twenty days reminds one more of Stakhanovite competition than archeology.

The fifty-one Shang-Yin period tombs are divided into five types in the brief report from the "Cultural Objects Working Battalion" of Honan.

Several things were unique about the single example of Type I. There was a smaller pit in the floor of the tomb below the pelvis and thighs of the corpse. (The excavators call it a *yao-k'eng,* a waist pit.) The burial contained no coffin. The funeral furnishings were laid on a shelflike niche cut into the wall of the grave a little distance above the place the corpse's head would be.

Type II, of which there were eight examples, all had either inner or outer coffins. On all four sides of the coffin marks there were two distinct layers of porous (untamped) earth.

Generally a dog was found to be buried over the corpse in these layers. Waist pits were present as well as coffins. The funeral furnishings were richer than in other type tombs.

There was only a single example of Type III, but it had been robbed. There was no waist pit apparent, however. As for Type IV, there were twenty-two examples. The earth fill had been tamped all the way, and a dog was buried in the waist pit and another atop the coffin. Generally there were no furnishings other than the coffin. There were eighteen examples of Type V, which were shallow earthen graves. Traces of wood remains were found only on the bottom. Some pottery and polished stone were present, but these graves had less furnishings than the others. In all Type V graves the area on the floor of the grave was strewn with cinnabar. This invariably had the same outlines as the ashy remains of the coffin bottom. It is possible that the coffin floor was covered with cinnabar. In a few tombs the excavators found imprints of designs from the coffin covers in red, yellow, black and white which were still fresh and brilliant when brought to the surface.

The bodies of thirty-one burials were extended, face up, with arms lying down along the sides. In three cases the body had been placed face downward in the coffin, with arms extended along the sides. The remainder were too badly disturbed or decomposed to discover the original posture. The statistical evidence (and indeed that is all that is available) not only confirms the fact that the north bank of the river was the land of the dead for the Shang capital, but indicates quite clearly that the tombs in this area next to the cotton factory were for those of rather modest estate for the most part.

Pottery vessels outnumber the bronze objects a hundred to one, yet because the graves are actually dug through the culture layer which is known to be Shang City-State in date, we know the tombs were late in the Bronze Age. The fact that many tombs are actually cut through other tombs of the same type and are crowded together, indicates that the area was used as a graveyard over a long period of time. The artifacts themselves all fall into what would be classified as Shang in type and period. The conclusion, then, is that this site was the burial place of many generations of Shang-Yin people right up to the time those tough warriors of the Chou period moved in on them and either captured and enslaved them or drove them out. Thus was brought to a close five hundred years of history in China, the key to which were the dragon bones that for thousands of years lay moldering in the yellow earth. Why the Shang-Yin people declined is just as much of a mystery as is the place from which they came.

TABLE OF TRADITIONAL DYNASTIC DATES

Period of legendary emperors	Fu Hsi	B.C.	2852
	Shen Nung	" "	2737
	Yellow Emperor	" "	2697
	Yao	" "	2356
	Shun	" "	2255
Hsia Dynasty (legendary?)	Yü The Great (flood controller)	" "	2205
Shang Dynasty	Ch'eng T'ang	" "	1766
	P'an-keng (moved to Shang City?)	" "	1401
	Wu-ting	" "	1198
Chou Dynasty	Wu Wang	" "	1122
	P'ing Wang ⎫ Ch'un-Ch'iu	" "	770
	Ching Wang ⎭ period	" "	519
	Yüan Wang ⎫ "Warring States"	" "	475
	Nan Wang ⎭ period	" "	314
Ch'in Dynasty	Shih-hwang	" "	221
Han Dynasty	Liu Pang	" "	206

Bibliography

Chapter 1

The *Bulletin of the Geological Survey of China* and the *Memoirs* of the same organization, published in Peking and New York, carry many detailed articles on this kind of "dragon bone." The numerous issues of these periodicals can be found in every large university library, but almost nowhere else.

Andersson, J. G., *Children of the Yellow Earth*, London, 1934. This treats most of the finds (in which he was involved) in a highly readable fashion. The book has long been out of print and should be republished.

Andrews, R. C., *Under a Lucky Star*, New York, 1943, *On the Trail of Ancient Man*, New York, 1926. Both of these give much of the romance of the Central Asiatic Expeditions and are filled with excellent photographs of the terrain and the sites involved.

Chapters 2, 3 and 4

The *Bulletin*, the *Memoirs*, and *Children of the Yellow Earth* are most informative for the events leading up to full scale excavation of the cave; the first two mentioned contain monographs on the fossils themselves.

Oakley, K. P., *Man the Toolmaker*, London, 1950.

Weidenreich, F., *Apes, Giants, and Men*, Chicago, 1947.
    The latter is a collection of Dr. Weidenreich's papers and lectures on the general topic of human evolution with special emphasis on the significance of Sinanthropus.

Chapter 5

Willetts, Wm., *Chinese Art* (I.II.), Pelican, 1958.
    Admirably summarizes the digs, finds and speculations. *Children of the Yellow Earth* again relates Andersson's part in the discoveries with a sort of windblown and sunburned charm. Andersson and Davidson Black publish the first accounts in the *Geological Survey, Memoirs,* and another series published by the Geological Survey of China becomes important; *Paleontologica Sinica.*

Andersson, J. G., *Researches into the Prehistory of the Chinese* (being #15 of the *Bulletin of the Museum of Far Eastern Antiquities*), Stockholm, 1943. This is a summary of Andersson's final thoughts about the time scale involved in the Painted Pottery sites, the relationships with more western cultures and the significance of his discoveries.

Chapter 6

Starr, M. K., (trans.) *Ch'eng-tzu Yai* (Yale Univ. Publications in Anthro. #56), New Haven, 1956.
    A meticulous translation of the report, by Li Chi and others, of this first all-Chinese dig which gives all the information there is on this type-site of the Lung-shan Culture; many drawings and maps.

Chapter 7

Anyang Fa-chüeh Pao-kao
Chia-ku-wen Hsüeh Nien-piao by Tung Tso-pin.
    Both of the above exist only in Chinese. They are the

source of most of the information in this and the next two chapters.

Creel, H. G., *The Birth of China,* New York, 1936 (1954).

An excellent, popular treatment of early Chinese culture which incorporates much information from the above works, and personal observations.

Menzies, J. M., *The Culture of the Shang Dynasty* in the Smithsonian Institution's Annual Report, 1931.

Somewhat outdated but it also includes personal observations.

Li, Chi, *The Beginnings of Chinese Civilization,* Seattle, 1957.

Disappointing in that its recent date would lead the reader to expect new information which, in fact, does not appear.

Chapter 8

Yetts, W. P., *Anyang: A Retrospect,* China Society, London, 1942.

This little pamphlet is difficult to obtain but has some fine speculations on the significance of the site.

Creel, H. G., *Studies in Early Chinese Culture,* First Series, Baltimore, 1937.

A much more scholarly and detailed monograph with some treatment of the Hsia dynasty and whether it ever existed.

Chapter 9

Loehr, M., "The Stratigraphy of Hsiao-T'un (Anyang)" in *Ars Orientalis,* II, pp. 440-457, 1957.

This is a translation of the summary of discoveries at Hsiao T'un which appeared in the *Chinese Journal of Archeology,* vol. 2, Shanghai, 1947, pp. 1-81.

Hansford, S. H., *A Visit to Anyang,* China Society, London, 1951.

White, W. C., *Bronze Culture of Ancient China,* Toronto, 1956.

Chapter 10

Britton, R. S., *Fifty Shang Inscriptions*, Princeton Library, 1940.
White, W. C., *Bone Culture of Ancient China*, Toronto, 1945.
The *Harvard Journal of Asiatic Studies*, vol. 11, 1-2 (1948).
    In this issue there is a brief but excellent article by Tung Tso-pin (in English) which was written more for the public than for the specialist.
Watson, Wm. *China: Before the Han Dynasty*, New York, 1961.
    The latest summary of important archeological facts and theories about China before the 2nd. century B.C.

Chapter 11

Yetts, W. P., *The George Eumorphopoulos Collection . . . of Bronzes*, London, 1929.
    There are a score of illustrated catalogs of bronzes, but this lavish and famous publication is perhaps the most satisfactory experience short of visiting museums with first class collections. A limited edition, it can only be had in the large public and university libraries. Willetts' *Chinese Art*, more easily obtainable, has good plates and a sound account of bronze working.
Loehr, M., *Chinese Bronze Age Weapons*, Ann Arbor, 1956.
    A catalog of the Werner Jannings collection of Chinese weapons (now in China), a long and thorough treatment of Anyang weapons and Siberian analogies, and a handsome publication.

Chapter 12

    Information on the present state of Chinese archeology can be had only from Chinese language sources, but the works below are by astute observers and will give the reader a very clear picture of conditions in China and of the atmosphere in which excavations are carried on.
Wilson, J. Tuzo, *One Chinese Moon*, Toronto, 1959.
Guillain, R., *600 Million Chinese*, New York, 1957.

Index